THE ILLUSTRATED DICTIONARY OF

EARTH
SCIENCES

Reader's notes

The entries in this dictionary have several features to help you broaden your understanding of the word you are looking up.

- Each entry is introduced by its headword. All the headwords in the dictionary are arranged in alphabetical order.

- Each headword is followed by a part of speech to show whether the word is used as a noun, adjective, verb or prefix.

- Each entry begins with a sentence that uses the headword as its subject.

- Words that are bold in an entry are cross references. You can look them up in the dictionary to find out more information about the topic.

- The sentence in italic at the end of an entry helps you to see how the headword can be used.

- Many of the entries are supported by illustrations. The labels on the illustrations highlight the key points of information and will help you to understand the correct scientific setting of the entry.

- Many of the labels on the illustrations have their own entries in the dictionary and can therefore be used as cross references.

THE ILLUSTRATED DICTIONARY OF

EARTH SCIENCES

Contributors
Martin Walters
Felicity Trotman

CLAREMONT
BOOKS

Copyright © 1995 Godfrey Cave Associates
First published 1995 in this format by
Claremont Books
42 Bloomsbury Street
London WC1B 3QJ

Design: Ann Samuel and Tracy Carrington
Illustrations: Ken Chatterton; Jeremy Gower and
Matthew White (B.L. Kearley Ltd); Jeremy Pyke;
Oxford Illustrators Ltd

Consultants: Patrick Spencer, B.A., postgraduate student, Department of
Geology, University of Bristol, Bristol, UK.
Dr R.J.G. Savage, B.Sc., PhD., Professor of vertebrate Palaeontology,
Department of Geology, University of Bristol, Bristol, UK.

Printed in Great Britain.

ISBN 1 85471 645 X

A

abrasion *noun*
Abrasion is the process of rubbing or wearing away. Sand blown by wind can rub away at rock faces, causing abrasion.
The rocks had been worn down by abrasion.

abrasive *noun*
An abrasive is a rough substance which is used for rubbing down or polishing something. **Emery** is an example of an abrasive found in nature.
Sand blown by wind acts as an abrasive.
abrasive *adjective*

abyss *noun*
An abyss is a deep cave or valley. A deep valley on the ocean floor is also often called an abyss.
The divers descended into the narrow abyss at the bottom of the sea.

abyssal plain *noun*
The abyssal plain is the name given to the deepest part of the ocean floor. It is almost level and lies at a depth of between about 4,000 metres and 6,000 metres.
No light ever reaches the abyssal plain.

acid *noun*
An acid is a kind of **chemical** which dissolves in water to make an acidic solution. Many acids can dissolve metals. An acid is the opposite of an **alkali**.
Strong acids are dangerous and can sting or burn the skin.
acidic *adjective*

acid rain *noun*
Acid rain is rain which is polluted by weak nitric and sulphuric acid. The acids are made when sulphur dioxide and nitric oxide, released into the air by burning **fossil fuels**, combine with water **vapour**.
Acid rain kills trees and fish and eats away rocks.

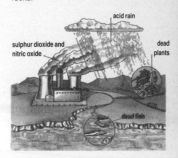

acid soil *noun*
Acid soil contains minerals rich in hydrogen and aluminium. Water **leaches** minerals, such as calcium, magnesium, potassium and sodium, out of the soil. Most plants need these minerals to grow.
Some mosses grow well in acid soil.

acid water *noun*
Acid water is water that contains weak carbonic acid. The water reacts with carbon dioxide in the **atmosphere** and in plants to make the acid. Carbonic acid reacts with many **minerals**.
The acid water turned the iron to rust.

active *adjective*
Active is a word which describes **volcanoes** that **erupt** from time to time. Volcanoes which have not erupted for a long period are called **dormant**.
Smoke poured out of the active volcano.

aeolian *adjective*
Aeolian is a word which describes the action of the **wind**. Aeolian **erosion** occurs when the wind carries sand or other hard particles and these wear away soil and rocks.
The scientists could see that the aeolian erosion was wearing away the surface of the rock.

aerial *adjective*
Aerial describes an object which is found in the air. Birds and other animals which feed on flying insects are known as aerial predators.
The shooting stars made a marvellous aerial display.

aftershock *noun*
Aftershock is the name given to shocks, or **tremors**, from an **earthquake**. The aftershock occurs minutes, hours or even months after the first shock of an earthquake has faded away.
The aftershock caused even more damage than the earthquake itself.

agate *noun*
Agate is a mineral. It is a form of **quartz**. Agate usually has a banded pattern on its surface. Polished agate is used in jewellery as a semi-precious stone.
Onyx is a black and white form of agate.

banded pattern

aggregate *noun*
An aggregate is a type of soil. It is made up of tiny rock particles that stick together. Aggregate also describes the sand and gravel that is mixed with **cement** to make concrete.
The bricklayers made concrete by mixing aggregate and cement.

agriculture *noun*
Agriculture describes how land is used for growing crops for food and for rearing animals.
Flat, fertile soils are the best for agriculture.

air *noun*
Air is the mixture of **gases** that surrounds the Earth. Air is mostly made up of **nitrogen** and **oxygen**. It also contains **carbon dioxide**, **argon** and water **vapour**.
The air was so clear that we could see the hills in the distance.

air pressure ▶ **atmospheric pressure**

alabaster *noun*
Alabaster is a mineral. It is a form of **gypsum**. Alabaster is a soft rock and can be carved easily. Alabaster can also be polished to give it a smooth, shiny surface.
She carved a model of a bird out of alabaster.

alkali *noun*
An alkali is a kind of chemical **compound** which can neutralize **acids**. An alkali is the opposite of an acid.
Some strong alkalis are used in industry to clean machinery.
alkaline *adjective*

alloy *noun*
An alloy is a kind of solid substance. An alloy is made by melting a **metal** and mixing in smaller amounts of other metals or non-metals. The mixture is then cooled until it becomes solid.
Brass is an alloy which is made from copper and zinc.

alluvial fan   *noun*
An alluvial fan is a fan-shaped spread of
gravel, **sand** or **soil** made by mountain
streams or **rivers**. When a stream leaves the
hills, it flows more slowly across a valley or
plain and makes an alluvial fan. Alluvial fans
are common in dry regions.
The soil of an alluvial fan may be very fertile.

alluvium   *noun*
Alluvium is a **deposit** of sand, **mud** or
gravel. Alluvium is left by a **river** when it
leaves hilly ground and flows more slowly
over flatter land.
The soil of the valley was a rich alluvium.

alpine   *adjective*
Alpine describes land above the **tree-line**
on **mountains**. The name comes from
the Alp mountains of Europe, but is used for
all such areas in the world. Alpine areas are
very rocky. The soil is usually shallow, and the
climate is cold.
*There was not enough soil in the alpine region
for a tree to grow roots.*

altimeter   *noun*
An altimeter is an instrument for measuring
height, or **altitude**. Some simple altimeters
work by measuring **atmospheric pressure**.
This grows weaker as the distance of the air
from Earth increases. Aircraft altimeters
measure the time it takes a radio signal to
travel from the aircraft to the ground and
back again.
*The pilot could tell how high up we were by
reading the altimeter.*

altitude   *noun*
Altitude describes the height of one point
above another point. The altitude of land is
usually measured from **sea-level**.
*Aircraft and migrating birds sometimes fly at
a very high altitude.*

altocumulus   *adjective*
Altocumulus describes a kind of **cloud**.
Altocumulus clouds are white, fluffy and
rounded and appear during fine weather.
*We could see a few altocumulus clouds in
the blue sky on the warm day.*

altostratus   *adjective*
Altostratus describes a kind of **cloud**.
Altostratus clouds are dark grey and form
a continuous sheet across the sky.
The altostratus clouds blotted out the Sun.

aluminium   *noun*
Aluminium is an **element**. It is a bright, silvery
metal. Aluminium is extracted from an ore
called **bauxite**, which is a kind of
aluminium oxide.
*Aluminium is useful for making machinery
and aircraft bodies because it is light
and strong.*

amber   *noun*
Amber is a **mineral** which can be used as a
gem. It can be clear orange or cloudy yellow.
Amber comes from the liquid sap, or resin,
which oozed from trees many millions of
years ago. Some pieces of amber have
insects trapped in them. Amber is found in
sedimentary rocks and washed up
on **sea-shores**.
*She wore a necklace made from
yellow amber.*

dial

needle

7

amethyst *noun*
Amethyst is a **mineral**. It is a precious stone which has a purple colour. Amethyst is a kind of **quartz**.
The brooch had a large amethyst in the centre.

ammonite *noun*
An ammonite was a kind of shellfish called a mollusc. It is now extinct. Ammonites had hard, chalky, spiral shells. The shells can be found as **fossils** in some kinds of **sedimentary** rock. Ammonite fossils are important in dating **zones** of **Mesozoic** rocks.
The fossil collection contained several large ammonites.

anemometer *noun*
An anemometer is an instrument which measures the speed of the **wind**. In the commonest type of anemometer, the wind turns small cups which are attached to a rod. The harder the wind is blowing, the faster the cups turn.
The anemometer showed that the wind was at storm force.

aneroid barometer *noun*
An aneroid barometer measures **atmospheric pressure**. An aneroid barometer contains a metal box with a **vacuum** inside. The box has flexible sides which change shape as the weight of the air above changes.
Aneroid barometers have mostly replaced the older mercury barometers.

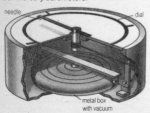

Antarctic Circle *noun*
The Antarctic Circle is an imaginary line around the Earth, surrounding **Antarctica**. The position of the Antarctic Circle is at 66 degrees 30 minutes south of the Equator.
The Antarctic Circle lies about 2,000 kilometres south of New Zealand.

Antarctica *noun*
Antarctica is the Earth's most southerly **continent**. Antarctica is the land around the South Pole. Most of the land is covered by **ice**. Antarctica is the coldest continent on Earth.
The scientists went to Antarctica to study different kinds of ice.

anthracite *noun*
Anthracite is a kind of **coal**. It is hard, black and shiny and is the purest form of coal. Anthracite is more than 90 per cent **carbon** and makes very little smoke when it burns.
She brought a bucket of anthracite into the house to burn on her fire.

anti- *prefix*
Anti- is a prefix meaning against or preventing.
He added antifreeze to the water to lower its freezing point.

8

anticline *noun*
An anticline is a fold in the **strata** of **rocks**. The fold has the shape of an arch, with the youngest **layers** of rocks at the top. Anticlines are caused by pressure on the rocks from the sides. The opposite of an anticline is a **syncline**.
The scientists studied the layers of different rocks they could see in the anticline.

rock strata

young rock

old rock

anticyclone *noun*
An anticyclone is an area of high **atmospheric pressure**. Anticyclones nearly always bring clear skies and settled **weather**. The opposite of an anticyclone is a **depression**, which is sometimes known as a **cyclone**.
The anticyclone brought hot, dry weather.

aquamarine *noun*
Aquamarine is a **mineral**. It is a precious stone with a green or turquoise colour. Aquamarine is a form of **beryl**.
He wore a ring which was set with aquamarine.

aqueous *adjective*
Aqueous describes substances which are like water, or which contain water.
The powder was dissolved in an aqueous solution.

Archean *adjective*
Archean is the name given to the second earliest **eon** in **geological time**. Some scientists believe the Archean Eon lasted from about 4,000 million years ago to about 2,500 million years ago. It is part of **Precambrian** time.
Many of the oldest rocks were formed during the Archean Eon.

archipelago *noun*
An archipelago is a group of **islands**. The islands in an archipelago are usually small, and they often form a line or a curved pattern. *The Society Islands form an archipelago in the south Pacific Ocean.*

Arctic *noun*
The Arctic is the name given to the most northerly region of the world. It lies within the **Arctic Circle**. Northern Canada, much of Greenland and the northern Soviet Union all lie within the Arctic region.
In some parts of the Arctic the seas are always frozen.

Arctic Circle *noun*
The Arctic Circle is an imaginary line around the Earth, to the north of which lies the **Arctic** region. The position of the Arctic Circle is at 66 degrees 17 minutes north of the **Equator**. *The island of Iceland lies just below the Arctic Circle.*

argon *noun*
Argon is an **element**. It is a **gas** which is found in the Earth's atmosphere. It makes up about 1 per cent of the air. Argon is an **inert** gas so it does not react with other chemicals and does not form **compounds**.
Some kinds of light bulb are filled with argon.

9

arid *adjective*
Arid describes parts of the Earth which have a very dry **climate**, such as hot **deserts**. Arid regions have very little rain, or lose any water that falls as rain by **evaporation**. Most arid regions lie in the **tropics**.
The soil was so arid that no crops would grow.

arroyo *noun*
An arroyo is a rocky **ravine**. Arroyos occur in dry areas and in **deserts**. They are a kind of dry river valley. They have steep sides and flat, sandy bottoms. Arroyos are found in the south-west of the United States of America, in parts of India and in South Africa.
The travellers found the heat of the arroyo too strong for walking.

artesian well *noun*
An artesian well is a well which provides **water** without pumping. The well draws up water which has been held under pressure between layers of **impermeable** rock.
The artesian well gave a continuous supply of water to the valley.

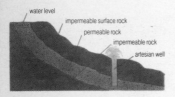

asbestos *noun*
Asbestos is a **mineral** with a rough, thread-like texture. It is a **silicate**. Asbestos does not burn and can be used to protect objects from damage by flames. Asbestos is also resistant to attack by most chemicals. Breathing asbestos dust is very harmful.
Asbestos can be woven into a cloth which resists heat.

asphalt *noun*
Asphalt is a thick, sticky substance. Asphalt forms when petroleum is distilled or when it evaporates.
Asphalt is mixed with stones or chippings for making roads or for covering roofs.

atlas *noun*
An atlas is a collection of **maps**. Some atlases include maps of the whole world, others may show details of just one or a few countries. Maps of the stars and planets can also be found in atlases.
They looked in the atlas to find a map of the Arctic region.

atmosphere *noun*
The atmosphere is the layer of **gases** around the **Earth**. The atmosphere can be divided into a number of smaller layers. The **troposphere** is nearest to the ground and contains the **air** we breathe.
Without the atmosphere, there would be no life on Earth.

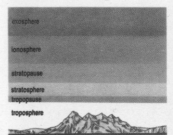

atmospheric pressure *noun*
Atmospheric pressure measures the weight of the **air** that presses down on the surface of the Earth. Atmospheric pressure is measured in **bars**.
Atmospheric pressure is highest at ground level or sea-level and gets lower with altitude.

atoll *noun*
An atoll is a circular **coral reef**. Small **islands**
form where the reef is higher than the sea.
In the centre of the atoll there is a shallow
lagoon. On its outer edge, the atoll often falls
steeply down towards the sea-bed.
The rocks of an atoll are made of coral.

aurora *noun*
An aurora is a coloured light which can
sometimes be seen in the sky at night,
especially in the **polar** regions. An aurora is
caused by electrical particles from the Sun
hitting **nitrogen** and **oxygen** atoms in the
Earth's **atmosphere**.
*The aurora lit up the night sky with an eerie
green glow.*

aurora australis *noun*
Aurora australis is the name of the **aurora**
that is sometimes seen in the skies above the
region surrounding the **South Pole**.
*Many people saw the wonderful colours of the
aurora australis.*

aurora borealis *noun*
Aurora borealis is the name of the **aurora** that
is sometimes seen in the skies above the
region surrounding the **North Pole**.
*The aurora borealis is also called the
Northern Lights.*

autumn *noun*
Autumn is the period in the year between
summer and winter in **temperate regions**.
Autumn is a time when daylight becomes
shorter and the weather may be cool and
misty. In some countries it is called the fall.
During autumn, the nights became frosty.

avalanche *noun*
An avalanche happens when **rocks** or **snow**
slide down the side of a **hill** or **mountain**. The
slide may contain large amounts of snow and
ice, mixed with rocks and stones. Avalanches
often take place in high mountains.
*Skiing in some places is dangerous because
of the risk of avalanches.*

axis *noun*
An axis is an imaginary line around which an
object rotates. The Earth rotates once around
its axis approximately every 24 hours. The
Earth's axis runs from the **North Pole** to the
South Pole. It crosses the **Equator**, which is
an imaginary line circling the Earth.
*Day and night are caused by the movement of
the Earth around its axis.*

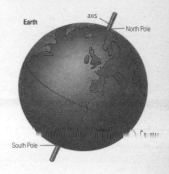

11

B

background radiation   *noun*

Background radiation is the name given to **radiation** that is always present on the Earth. Background radiation comes from the natural decay of **minerals** such as **radium** and **uranium** in the rocks and soil. Some radiation comes from rays reaching the Earth from space.
The radium in the rocks beneath Kerala, in India, produces a high level of background radiation.

bank   *noun*

A bank is the raised **ridge** of rock or soil at the edge of a **river**. The two banks hold the **channel** in which the water flows. Bank is also used to describe a large solid mass of **cloud** in the sky.
During the flood, the water flowed over the bank of the river.

bar   *noun*

Bar is the unit used for measuring the weight of air or **atmospheric pressure**. Normal atmospheric pressure at **sea-level** is about one bar, or 1,000 millibars. Bar can also be used to describe a **sandbar** in a **river** or an **estuary**.
Atmospheric pressure is measured in bars or millibars.

barium   *noun*

Barium is an **element**. It is a soft, white **metal** that is very heavy. Other elements can mix easily with barium. Barium is obtained from the **mineral** barytes.
Many compounds of barium are used in industry.

barograph   *noun*

A barograph measures changes in **atmospheric pressure** which may take place over a period of time. In a barograph, a pen attached to an **aneroid barometer** makes a mark on paper on a moving drum. The drum turns at a steady speed, so that the pen can draw a line to show the changing pressure.
He read the barograph to see how the atmospheric pressure had changed.

moving drum   pen   aneroid barometer   chart

barometer   *noun*

A barometer is an instrument which is used for measuring **atmospheric pressure**. An **aneroid barometer** has a dial marked in units of pressure. A needle moves over this dial as the atmospheric pressure changes. Another kind of barometer measures atmospheric pressure with a column of **mercury**.
Forecasters use barometers to work out how the weather is about to change.

barrier reef   *noun*

A barrier reef is a kind of **coral reef**. It is a long reef which lies at the edge of the **continental shelf** just a little way from the **sea-shore**. A barrier reef is separated from the mainland by a channel of shallow sea.
The most famous barrier reef is the Great Barrier Reef off the east coast of Australia.

basalt   *noun*

Basalt is a kind of **igneous** rock or **stone**. Basalt is a dark colour and looks as though it is made up of very tiny pieces of rock. Basalt develops from **lava** and is one of the main kinds of rock that make up the Earth's **crust**.
Basalt is a very hard rock which is often used by builders.

basin *noun*

A basin is a **hollow** in the landscape. It has smooth sides and is shaped like a bowl.
A basin is also the area of land drained by a **river** and its **tributaries**.
We could see the hills rising at the sides of the basin.

bathyscaph *noun*

A bathyscaph is a kind of small, **submersible vehicle** used to explore deep water.
A bathyscaph usually has room for just one or two people who can look out at the sea through the windows in safety. It can move about freely under the water.
The bathyscaph took them slowly down towards the sea-bed.

compartment for scientists and equipment

hull

bauxite *noun*

Bauxite is a **mineral** which contains the metal **aluminium**. It is found mostly in the warmer parts of the world. Almost all aluminium is obtained from bauxite.
The earth had been removed from one side of the hill to mine the bauxite underneath.

bay *noun*

A bay is an area of the sea which is enclosed by a curved section of **coast**. Bays vary in size from a few hundred metres to thousands of kilometres across. The Bay of Bengal is the name of the huge bay in the Indian Ocean which lies between India and Burma.
He saw the lighthouse shining across the water from the other side of the bay.

beach *noun*

A beach is the strip of sloping land which lies along the **sea-shore** between the high and low water level of the **tides**. Beaches are usually made of sand, gravel or pebbles.
A beach is formed by the action of waves washing small pieces of material from the rocks or soil at the land's edge and grinding them down.
The beach at the base of the cliff sloped down into the sea.

beacon *noun*

A beacon is a light or other signal which can be easily seen. Beacons are used to guide ships and aeroplanes on a safe course.
A beacon is also a hill where signal fires used to be lit.
The lighthouse acted as a beacon to warn the fishing boat that it was near rocks.

bearing *noun*

A bearing is a way of measuring direction. Ships at sea work out their direction in bearings. These are measured in degrees, using a compass.
The climber used a compass to find his way in the mountains.

North

direction of travel ⟶

compass

Beaufort Scale ▶ page 14

bed *noun*

A bed is a word used in **geology** to describe a **layer**, or **stratum**, of **sedimentary** rock.
They found the fossils close together in the same bed of rock.

Beaufort Scale *noun*

The Beaufort Scale is a scale that is used to measure the force of the **wind**. The scale goes from calm, force 0, to **hurricane**, force 12.
A storm is force 10 on the Beaufort Scale.

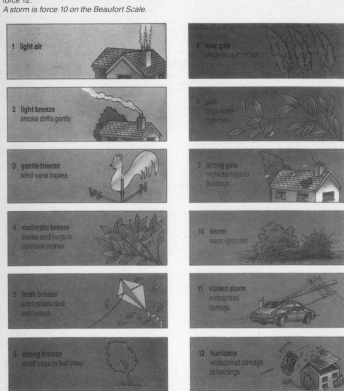

1 light air

2 light breeze
smoke drifts gently

3 gentle breeze
wind vane moves

4 moderate breeze
leaves and twigs in
constant motion

5 fresh breeze
wind raises dust
and leaves

6 strong breeze
small trees in leaf sway

7 near gale
whole trees in motion

8 gale
twigs break
from trees

9 strong gale
slight damage to
buildings

10 storm
trees uprooted

11 violent storm
widespread
damage

12 hurricane
widespread damage
to buildings

bedrock *noun*

Bedrock is the solid rock beneath the surface of the Earth. In most places, the bedrock is covered by layers of loose rock or soil.
After digging down through the soil, we came to the hard bedrock.

benthic *adjective*

Benthic describes the area at the bottom of the sea. It also describes the animals and plants living there. On the **continental shelf** and near the **sea-shore**, the benthic zone is quite shallow. In the deep sea, the benthic zone is 1,000 metres in depth. The opposite of benthic is **pelagic**.
They used a trawl net to collect benthic fish from the sea-bed.

benthos *noun*

Benthos is the name used for the plants and animals living on the sea-bed, or in the **benthic** zone. The benthos includes seaweeds, and sea creatures such as crabs, shellfish and flatfish.
The benthos of the continental shelf is very varied.

beryl *noun*

Beryl is a **mineral**. It is found mostly in **granite** rocks. Beryl contains the elements **beryllium**, **aluminium**, **silicon** and **oxygen**. The metal beryllium is made from beryl **crystals**.
The precious stones emerald and aquamarine are forms of beryl.

beryllium *noun*

Beryllium is an **element**. It is a **metal** which is similar to **aluminium** and is used for making **alloys**. Beryllium is found in the mineral **beryl**.
The factory made beryllium from ore containing beryl.

bight *noun*

A bight is a very large **bay**. It is surrounded by the lands of a **continent**.
The Bight of Benin lies off the west coast of Africa.

bio- *prefix*

Bio- is a prefix used to refer to living things.
The biochemist studied the chemistry of animals and plants.

biogas *noun*

Biogas is a gas given off when waste materials **decompose**. The main gas produced in this way is **methane**. Methane can be collected and burned to provide heat **energy**.
Manure and food waste are good sources of biogas.

biological *adjective*

Biological describes anything to do with living organisms. For example, biological science is the study of living things.
The region's unusual animals and plants proved to be of great biological interest.

biomass *noun*

Biomass is a word which describes the total amount of living things in a particular area.
An area of rain forest has a large biomass.

biosphere *noun*

The biosphere is the name given to the parts of the Earth where living things are found. The biosphere is also called the **global** ecosystem.
The atmosphere, the seas and the surface of the Earth all make up the biosphere.

bismuth *noun*
Bismuth is an **element** and a metal. **Alloys** of
bismuth melt at low temperatures. They are
used as a safety device in many machines
because they melt first, before the machines
get too hot. When the alloys melt, the
machines stop working. Bismuth is also used
to make some medicines.
There are large deposits of bismuth in Bolivia.

bitumen *noun*
Bitumen is an oily **compound** formed by the
evaporation of petroleum. Solid forms of
bitumen are also called **asphalt**.
*The intense heat of the midday Sun melted
the bitumen on the road.*

blizzard *noun*
A blizzard is a fierce **storm** of **snow**. Blizzards
are common in open, icy regions such as the
Arctic and **Antarctica**.
*During a blizzard, snow is often blown into
deep drifts.*

block mountain *noun*
A block mountain is a **mountain** formed when
two parts of the Earth's **crust** collide with
each other, trapping a third part. The trapped
section is pushed up between the other parts
to form a mountain. Block mountains are
often flat at the top, like Table Mountain in
South Africa.
*The block mountain towered over the
surrounding land.*

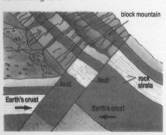

block mountain

fault   fault   rock strata
Earth's crust   Earth's crust

blowhole *noun*
A blowhole is a hole or **cave** in a sea **cliff**.
When the **tide** is high, the sea sprays out of
the blowhole. Blowholes are found in areas
where some of the rock in the cliffs has been
eroded more than others. Large waves trap
air in the caves, which then escapes as a
spray through the blowhole.
*As the waves entered the cave, sea water
spouted out through the blowhole.*

bluff *noun*
A bluff is a steep **cliff**. Bluffs may be found at
the edge of a **valley**, or at the **sea-shore**.
*The climber stopped at the top of the bluff to
get a good look at the valley below.*

bog *noun*
A bog is an area of marshy ground where the
soil is made up of wet **peat**. Bogs contain
many thousands of moss plants. These grow
in **water** and are known as bog mosses.
When the older moss plants die, their remains
gradually **decompose**. In most bogs, a new
layer of plants will grow on top of the dead
material.
The soil in the bog was very acidic.

borax *noun*
Borax is a **mineral**. It contains the elements
boron, **sodium**, **hydrogen** and **oxygen**.
Borax is used for softening water and for
cleaning.
*Borax is used to make a special kind of glass
which does not melt or crack when heated.*

bore *noun*
A bore is a kind of **wave** which moves steadily up a **river**, travelling against the usual flow of the water. Bores can be seen in funnel-shaped **estuaries** during very high **tides**.
In the Severn River in the British Isles, a famous bore can be seen when the tide flows towards the land.

bore *verb*
Bore is the word used to describe drilling through rocks. Special drills have to be used to bore through hard rocks and the process takes a long time.
The teams worked for many months to bore a tunnel through the cliffs.

boreal *adjective*
Boreal describes a **region** of the Earth. The boreal region lies south of the **Arctic**. In the boreal region, the main type of vegetation is the boreal forest, or **taiga**. These forests are made up mostly of coniferous trees.
The boreal forests of Siberia stretch for thousands of kilometres.

boron *noun*
Boron is an **element**. The element is rare and is only found as **compounds** with other substances. Boron is usually found in the form of boric acid or as **borax**.
They extracted the boron from rocks containing borax.

boulder *noun*
A boulder is a large **rock** which usually has rounded sides. Boulders are often found on mountain sides, at the foot of **cliffs** or **scree** slopes.
We sheltered from the wind behind a boulder.

breach *noun*
A breach is a crack or hole in a hard surface. During a violent storm, **breakers** may make a breach in a sea-wall. The action of **weathering** may cause a breach in a rock face.
The breach in the river bank caused the fields to be flooded.

breaker *noun*
A breaker is a kind of **wave**. Breakers are very large and powerful and occur on **coasts** which face the open **ocean**. Breaker waves are common on **reefs**.
The boy went surfing in the huge breakers off the coast of Australia.

breccia *noun*
Breccia is a kind of **sedimentary** rock. Breccia has a very coarse texture. It is made up of many sharp-sided pieces of rock of different sizes. These pieces of rock are cemented together.
The rocks at the sides of the valley contained large amounts of breccia.

breeze *noun*
A breeze is a **wind** of medium strength. Breezes can vary from light to strong. A light breeze makes leaves rustle and blows at about 6 kilometres an hour. A strong breeze makes large branches sway and blows at about 45 kilometres an hour. Breezes measure between 2 and 6 on the **Beaufort Scale**.
The boat's sails began to fill out in the breeze.

brook *noun*
A brook is a small, clear **stream** which is often found in hilly areas.
The brook flowed swiftly over the stones.

brown coal ► lignite

17

C

buoy *noun*
A buoy is a floating marker in the sea or in a
river. Safe **channels** of deeper water are
often shown by a line of buoys. Buoys also
mark shallow water near the **coast**.
*We steered the boat clear of the mud banks
by following the buoys.*

isolated danger mark

safe water mark

bush *noun*
Bush is a word that describes a habitat with
many scattered trees and shrubs. Large
areas of southern Africa and Australia are
covered by bush.
The bush was so dry it caught fire easily.

butte *noun*
A butte is a flat-topped **hill** with steep rocky
sides that is found in **arid** regions. A butte is
formed when a **plateau** is **eroded** at
the sides.
*The butte stood out clearly from the plain
below it.*

rock strata

cadmium *noun*
Cadmium is an **element**. It is a bluish-white
metal. Cadmium is often found in the same
rocks as **copper** and **zinc**. Cadmium is used
for making **alloys**. **Compounds** of cadmium
are used in making television sets and
batteries. Most cadmium comes from Japan.
Cadmium compounds are very poisonous.

calcite *noun*
Calcite is a white or colourless **mineral**.
It is made up of **crystals** of calcium
carbonate. Most kinds of **limestone** are made
of calcite.
*We could see each crystal of calcite without
using a microscope.*

calcium *noun*
Calcium is a common **element**. It is a **metal**
which forms many **compounds** with other
elements and is not found naturally in a pure
form. **Limestone** is made of calcium, **carbon**
and **oxygen**. Plants and animals need
calcium to grow properly.
*He drank milk to make sure there was enough
calcium in his diet.*

caldera *noun*
A caldera is a circular hole. A caldera is made
when a **volcano** erupts several times, losing
the **cone** at the top of the volcano. This leaves
a large hole shaped like a **basin** at the centre
of the volcano. A caldera can also be formed
by the **erosion** of an **extinct** volcano.
Sometimes, a lake fills the bottom of
the caldera.
*When we reached the edge of the caldera, we
could see right down into the lake.*

calm *adjective*
Calm describes gentle **weather** or sea conditions. In calm weather, there is little or no wind or rain. The opposite of calm is stormy. A calm sea has a flat surface or only very small waves.
They put the boat to sea in calm weather.

Cambrian *adjective*
Cambrian describes a **period** in **geological time**. The Cambrian Period lasted from about 590 million years ago to about 505 million years ago.
During the Cambrian Period, the climate was warm and wet.

canal *noun*
A canal is a straight waterway, built to carry ships or boats. Some canals link rivers together. Others connect two different **seas** or **oceans**. The Panama Canal, in Central America, allows ships to pass from the Atlantic Ocean to the Pacific Ocean and back. The Suez Canal links the Mediterranean Sea with the Red Sea.
The barges carried their cargo slowly along the canal.

canyon *noun*
A canyon is a deep **valley** with very steep sides. Canyons are usually found in flat, dry places and often have a river flowing in them. Some canyons are found on the **sea-bed**.
The Grand Canyon, in the United States of America, is one of the natural wonders of the world.

cape *noun*
A cape is a piece of **land** sticking out into a **sea**. One of the most famous is the Cape of Good Hope, on the coast of South Africa.
The ship sailed round the cape.

carbon *noun*
Carbon is a non-metallic **element**. Carbon is one of the commonest elements. It is found in all living things, as well as in rocks, **coal**, **oil** and other **minerals**. There are two forms of pure carbon. These are **graphite** and **diamond**.
All living things are made of compounds which contain carbon.

diamond   graphite

carbon dating *noun*
Carbon dating is a way of finding the age of an **organic** substance. Carbon dating measures the **radioactivity** of a kind of carbon called carbon-14, which all organic substances contain.
The scientists found the age of the fossil tree by carbon dating.

carbon dioxide *noun*
Carbon dioxide is a colourless **gas**. It has no smell. The gas is formed when **compounds** containing **carbon** are burned and when animals and plants breathe. Carbon dioxide makes up a tiny fraction of the air.
Plants make their food from carbon dioxide.

carbon monoxide *noun*
Carbon monoxide is a colourless **gas** which has no smell. This gas is very poisonous to breathe. Carbon monoxide is formed when **compounds** containing **carbon** are burned, but are not burned completely.
Exhaust from motor cars contains a mixture of poisonous gases, including carbon monoxide.

19

carbonate *noun*
A carbonate is a **salt** which is made from
carbon and another **element**. **Chalk** and
limestone are made up of calcium carbonate.
Washing soda contains sodium carbonate.
*Scientists found the water to be rich in
calcium carbonate.*

Carboniferous *adjective*
Carboniferous describes a **period** in
geological time. The Carboniferous Period
lasted from about 360 million years ago to
about 286 million years ago.
*Coal comes from the remains of trees and
other plants which grew during the
Carboniferous Period.*

cardinal point *noun*
A cardinal point is any one of the four main
points of the **compass**. The cardinal points
are north, south, west and east.
*The compass had the cardinal points clearly
marked on its face.*

carnelian *noun*
Carnelian, or cornelian, is a semi-precious
stone. It is a red or reddish-brown form of
chalcedony. Carnelian is found mostly in
India, South America and Japan. It has been
used as a gem for thousands of years.
The ring had a carnelian at its centre.

cartography *noun*
Cartography is the process of making **maps**.
A cartographer marks features of the land or
sea on a map by symbols, **contour** lines and
shading.
*He used cartography to make an atlas of
the world.*

cascade *noun*
A cascade is a series of **waterfalls** close
together on a river. Cascades are usually
found on fast-flowing rivers in mountain
areas.
She could not canoe through the cascade.

cassiterite *noun*
Cassiterite is a **mineral**. It is brown or black
and contains **tin** and **oxygen**. Cassiterite is
found mostly in **igneous** rocks.
The factory extracted tin from cassiterite.

cat's eye *noun*
Cat's eye is a precious stone. The pattern on
it looks like a cat's eye. Cat's eye is a form of
quartz. It is found mainly in Sri Lanka.
*The basket of precious stones contained
several shining cat's eyes.*

cataract *noun*
A cataract is a kind of **waterfall**. In a cataract,
the water flows very fast over a series of rocky
falls. Cataracts are found in mountain areas
where streams and rivers flow quickly.
*We had to land the boat because it was
getting close to the cataract.*

catchment area *noun*
A catchment area is a piece of land drained by
a **river** system. At the edge of one catchment
area, the water drains in another direction into
a different catchment area.
*The rivers at either side of the valley were in
the same catchment area.*

cave ► page 22

cavern ► **cave**

Celsius *noun*
Celsius is the name of the standard international **scale** which is used for measuring **temperature**. The Celsius scale is sometimes called the centigrade scale.
Water freezes at 0 degrees Celsius and boils at 100 degrees Celsius.

cement *noun*
Cement is a substance which sticks other materials together. In **sedimentary** rocks, cement is the material that binds pieces of rock together. Cement is also the name for a powdery mixture of **clay** and **lime**, which sets hard when water is added
The cement set hard and held the post upright.

Cenozoic *adjective*
Cenozoic describes the most recent **era** in **geological time**. The Cenozoic Era began about 65 million years ago and continues to the present day. It contains the **Quaternary** and **Tertiary** sub-eras.
Few mammals lived before the Cenozoic Era.

centigrade ► **Celsius**

chalcedony *noun*
Chalcedony is a **mineral**. It is a variety of **quartz** and is found in **volcanic** rocks. Many semi-precious **gems** are forms of chalcedony. Chalcedony is found all over the world.
Agate, onyx and bloodstone are all forms of chalcedony.

chalk *noun*
Chalk is a kind of **limestone** rock which is often pure white. It is made from the tiny shells of marine animals which died millions of years ago during the **Cretaceous** Period. Chalk is mostly calcium carbonate.
The White Cliffs of Dover in the British Isles are made of chalk.

channel *noun*
A channel is a groove in the Earth's surface cut by a river or a stream. The channel is cut out, or **eroded**, by the force of the flowing water. Near its source in high regions, a river flows down a rocky, narrow channel. In lowland areas, where the land slopes more gently, the channel fills up with **silt** and becomes wider.
During the floods, the river broke the banks of its usual channel.

chart *noun*
A chart is a kind of **map**. Weather forecasters use charts showing the **wind**, **temperature** and **atmospheric pressure**. Sailors also use charts to map their position at sea.
The chart showed the position of the rocks.

chemical *noun*
A chemical is any one of the individual, pure substances from which all materials are made. The simplest chemicals are the **elements**. Elements join together to make more complicated chemicals called **compounds**.
The scientist found out which chemicals were in the sample of rock.

chert *noun*
Chert is a kind of **sedimentary** rock. This rock is often a dark colour and is made up of tiny **crystals** of **quartz**. Chert usually forms on the sea floor. **Flint** is one kind of chert.
Part of the cliff was made of grey chert.

cave *noun*

A cave is a natural underground **hollow** found
in **rock**, **earth** or **ice**. Caves are usually made
by the action of **water** wearing away the rock,
soil or ice. Very large caves are sometimes
found in limestone rocks.
*The waves had carved out a huge cave in
the cliff.*

impervious rock

pot hole

fissures

cave

limestone

fissures

water table

calcite deposits

sink-hole

fault line

stalactite

stalagmite

impervious rock

China clay *noun*

China clay, or kaolin, is a **mineral**. It contains **aluminium** and **silica**. China clay is used for making china and porcelain and also for making some kinds of paper.
The potter made a jug from China clay.

chinook *noun*

The chinook is a kind of **wind**. The chinook is warm and dry and blows down the eastern side of the Rocky Mountains in the United States of America.
When the chinook blew, the snow melted very quickly.

chlorine *noun*

Chlorine is an **element**. It is a greenish-yellow **gas**. In nature, it is only found in **compounds**, such as sodium chloride, which is the chemical name for common salt.
Chlorine is added to the water in swimming pools to kill germs.

chromium *noun*

Chromium is an **element**. It is a hard, shiny metal. Chromium is used as a coating on steel to protect it from rust. Chromium is also used in **alloys**.
The bumper of the motor car was covered with a shiny coating of chromium.

cinnabar *noun*

Cinnabar is a reddish **mineral** found mostly in **volcanic** rocks. Cinnabar is made of soft, red **crystals**. It contains **mercury** and **sulphur**. It is occasionally used as a gemstone.
The factory extracted mercury from cinnabar.

circulation *noun*

Circulation describes a movement in the air or water. The circulation of the water in the sea creates regular **currents**. The circulation of the air makes winds blow.
The circulation of water in the ocean kept the sea cool near the coast.

cirrocumulus *adjective*

Cirrocumulus describes a kind of **cloud**. Cirrocumulus clouds are made of ice crystals. They can be found in the sky above a height of 5,000 metres. The clouds look like strips with rounded edges.
The sky was striped with cirrocumulus clouds.

cirrostratus *adjective*

Cirrostratus describes a kind of **cloud**. Cirrostratus clouds form high up and look like a thin veil across the sky. These clouds form as a **warm front** approaches.
The thin layer of cirrostratus clouds gradually covered the sky.

cirrus *adjective*

Cirrus describes a kind of **cloud**. Cirrus clouds form in the sky at a height of about 5,000 metres. The clouds have a wispy shape.
We saw thin bands of cirrus clouds high in the sky.

itrine *noun*

Citrine is a **mineral**. It is a yellow form of **quartz**. Citrine is very similar to **topaz**. It is found in parts of North America, South America, Russia and the British Isles. Some citrines are cut and used as gemstones.
The rock contained pale yellow crystals of citrine.

lay *noun*

Clay is a mud-like substance formed from tiny pieces of rock. The **minerals** in clay are mostly made from **silicates**. Clay soaks up water easily and becomes sticky and soft. It cracks when dry.
We waded into the river and the clay on the bottom stuck to our feet.

leavage *noun*

Cleavage describes the splitting of a rock or mineral to make flat surfaces. Some forms of cleavage are very unusual and are only seen when one particular mineral is split.
The geologist tapped the mineral sharply with a hammer, to show the cleavage.

liff *noun*

A cliff is a steep rock face rising up from flat ground or the side of a mountain. Many rocky **islands** have high cliffs. Cliffs are very common at the **coast**, where waves have **eroded** the rocks.
The captain could not land the boat because the island was surrounded by steep cliffs.

limate ► page 26

limatologist *noun*

A climatologist is someone who studies the **climate**. A climatologist describes the climates of the world and explains how these climates differ from place to place.
The climatologist warned that the climate might change.

loud ► page 30

cloudburst *noun*

A cloudburst is a sudden, very heavy shower of rain. Cloudbursts usually happen in warm and stormy weather.
They were quickly soaked by the unexpected cloudburst.

coal *noun*

Coal is a kind of **deposit** which is rich in **carbon**. Coal forms when **organic** material, such as trees and other plants, is crushed for millions of years by layers of **sedimentary** rock. Coal is a **fossil fuel**.
Coal gives out plenty of heat when it is burned.

coast *noun*

The coast is the edge of the land where it meets the sea. Some coasts are gently sloping, with sandy **beaches**. Other coasts are wild and rocky.
The coast was rich in fossils.

cobalt *noun*

Cobalt is an **element**. Cobalt is a **metal** that is used in making **magnets** and steel **alloys**. A **compound** of cobalt is also used to make a bright blue colour for paints.
The television set contained magnets made of cobalt.

climate *noun*

Climate describes the usual **weather** of a place or region. The climate can be affected by **temperature**, **rainfall**, **altitude** and distance from the sea. **Polar**, **temperature**, **maritime**, **tropical**, **arid** and Mediterranean are some of the major kin climate in the world.

Countries close to the Equator have a tr climate.

warm temperate climate

- dry summer (Mediterranean)
- dry winter
- no dry season

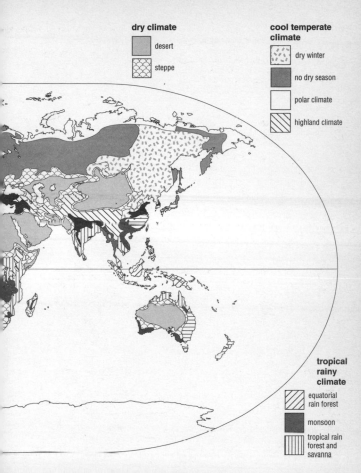

dry climate

- desert
- steppe

cool temperate climate

- dry winter
- no dry season
- polar climate
- highland climate

tropical rainy climate

- equatorial rain forest
- monsoon
- tropical rain forest and savanna

col *noun*

A col is a gap in a mountain or in a line of hills. A col is often the point where roads and railways cross the mountains or hills because it is lower than the rest of the area. A col can also be known as a **pass** or saddle.

We walked through the col from one valley to the next.

cold front *noun*

A cold front is the meeting place between a mass of warm air and a mass of cold air. A cold front arrives when a **depression** passes, bringing colder air and higher pressure. **Cumulonimbus clouds** may form at a cold front.

The temperature fell very quickly as the cold front passed.

compass *noun*

A compass is used for working out a direction. Most compasses contain a needle which has been made into a **magnet**. This always points to the Earth's **magnetic poles**.

We knew which way to go because we had a map and a compass.

glass

magnetic needle

composition *noun*

The composition of a substance is the total of all the **chemicals** that are in it. The composition of the air is a mixture of gases, mainly nitrogen and oxygen.

The chemist tried to discover the exact composition of the sample.

compound *noun*

A compound is a **chemical** substance which contains two or more **elements** joined together. Sodium chloride, or common salt, is a well-known chemical compound.

The chemist split the compound into its individual elements.

condensation *noun*

Condensation describes how a **gas** changes into a liquid. The most usual kind of condensation is the change from water **vapour** to water. **Clouds** are formed by condensation of water vapour in the **atmosphere**. The word condensation is also used for the liquid itself.

The cold glass clouded over with condensation when he breathed on it.

condense *verb*

cone *noun*

A cone is a solid shape which is circular at the bottom and pointed at the top. A **volcano** is often described as cone-shaped. During an **eruption**, the top of the volcano's cone may be blown away.

The cone of the volcano could be seen from every part of the country.

conglomerate *noun*

Conglomerate is a kind of **sedimentary** rock. It is made up of small, rounded pebbles held together by a **cement**. The cement is usually made up of **calcites** or **silicates**.

Conglomerate often forms along river beds or at beaches.

contaminate *verb*
To contaminate is to make something less pure by adding another substance. Dangerous **chemicals** may contaminate drinking water.
The air was contaminated by the dirty smoke.
contamination *noun*

continent ► page 34

continental crust *noun*
The continental crust is part of the outer shell of the Earth. The continental crust lies under the **continents**. The continental crust has an average depth of about 35 kilometres. **Tectonic plates** are made up of continental crust and **oceanic crust**.
All the continents lie on the continental crust.

continental divide *noun*
A continental divide is a chain of high mountains which separates one part of a **continent** from another.
The Rocky Mountains form a continental divide in North America.

continental drift *noun*
Continental drift describes how **continents** move over the surface of the Earth. Some scientists think that all the continents have gradually moved apart from one large land mass, called **Pangaea**, by continental drift. Continental drift is part of the study of **plate tectonics**.
Some scientists believe that, millions of years in the future, continental drift will move Australia nearer to Asia.

continental shelf *noun*
The continental shelf is the land which lies under the sea surrounding the **continents**. The width of the shelf varies from a few kilometres to about 400 kilometres. It slopes gently seawards. At the edge of the continental shelf, the sea-bed drops away very steeply.
Countries bordering the Pacific Ocean often have a narrow continental shelf.

contour *noun*
A contour is a line drawn on a **map**, or **chart**. All the points joined by a contour line on a map are the same height above **sea-level**. Maps of the land have contours to show high and low ground. Maps of the sea have contours showing the depth of the water.
The contours showed that the hill was steep.

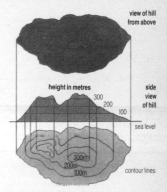

view of hill from above

height in metres 300 200 100

side view of hill

sea level

300m 200m 100m

contour lines

convection *noun*
Convection describes the way in which a hot gas or liquid moves. If air or water is heated from below, it warms up. As this happens, the air or water takes up more space and starts to rise. As it rises, the air or water cools down. A cool substance takes up less space, so it then begins to fall.
The hot, sandy soil warmed the air above and made it rise by convection.

convection current *noun*
A convection current is the movement of a **gas** such as air caused by **convection**. During convection, the air or gas moves up or down. The movement is called a **current**.
Convection currents of air often develop above the ground on a sunny day.

cloud *noun*

A cloud is a collection of water **vapour** or ice crystals. We can see clouds in the sky. Water drops form in clouds and fall as rain towards the ground. Some clouds form high in the **atmosphere**. Clouds which form close to the ground are called **mist** or **fog**.
The cloud rolled over the valley and covered the top of the hill.

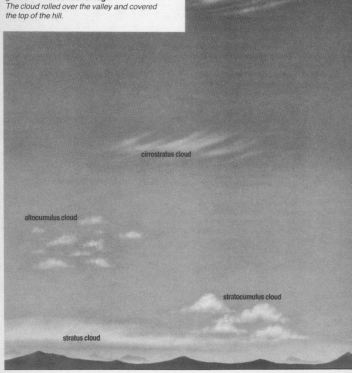

cirrus cloud

cirrostratus cloud

altocumulus cloud

stratocumulus cloud

stratus cloud

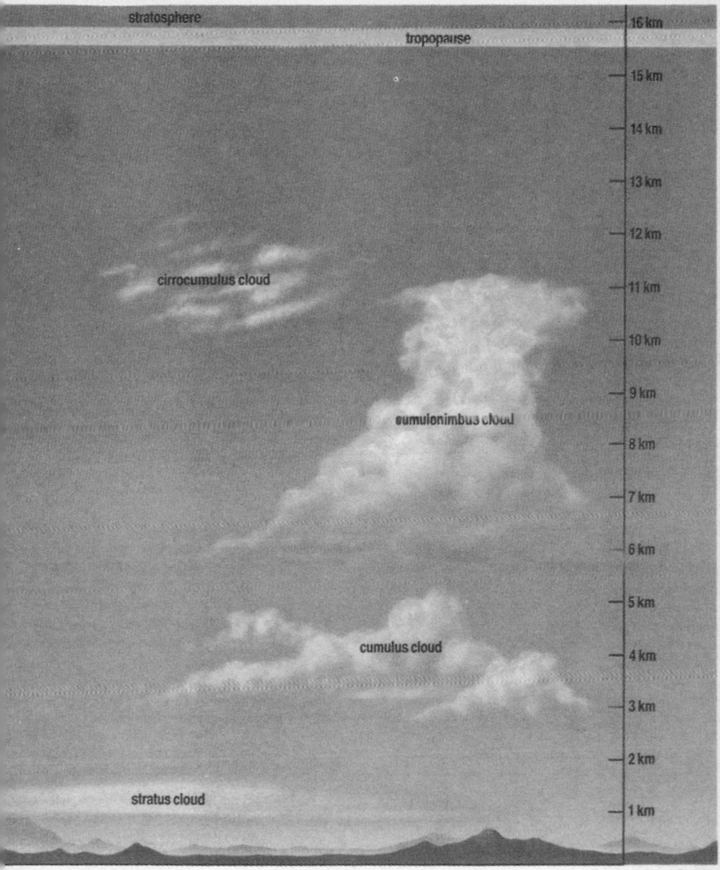

stratosphere

tropopause

— 16 km

— 15 km

— 14 km

— 13 km

— 12 km

cirrocumulus cloud

— 11 km

— 10 km

— 9 km

cumulonimbus cloud

— 8 km

— 7 km

— 6 km

— 5 km

cumulus cloud

— 4 km

— 3 km

— 2 km

stratus cloud

— 1 km

copper *noun*
Copper is an **element**. It is a soft, red-brown metal. Electric wire and cooking pots are sometimes made from copper. The metal is also used to make **alloys**.
He stripped the plastic from the copper wire.

coral *noun*
A coral is a kind of **marine** animal which has a hard skeleton. Corals belong to the same family as sea anemones. When the corals die, the skeletons build up to form a **coral reef**.
The warm sea contained millions of corals.

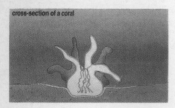
cross-section of a coral

coral island *noun*
A coral island is an island formed from a **coral reef**. Coral islands develop when the sea-level drops and the reef shows above the surface of the water.
The coral island was surrounded by white, sandy beaches.

coral reef *noun*
A coral reef is a rock-like structure formed in clear, warm seas by colonies of small animals called **corals**. Their chalky skeletons build up over hundreds of years to make coral reefs.
The coral reef was dangerous to ships.

corals

cordillera *noun*
A cordillera is a group or chain of **mountains**, stretching across the land in a line. The Andes, in South America, are a famous cordillera.
We could see the long line of the cordillera in the distance.

core *noun*
The core is the innermost part of the **Earth**, below the **mantle**. The core lies about 2,900 kilometres below the surface of the Earth. There is an **inner core** and an **outer core**. The inner core is solid and is made mostly of **iron** and **nickel**. The outer core is liquid and is made mainly of molten rocks. The temperature of the core is about 2,700 degrees Celsius.
Scientists think the inner core of the Earth is very dense.

cornelian ▶ **carnelian**

corundum *noun*
Corundum is a very hard **mineral**. It is made up of **aluminium** and **oxygen**. Red ruby and blue sapphire are forms of corundum. They are precious stones and are used to make jewellery. A very dark-coloured form of corundum is used in industry as an **abrasive**.
Ruby and sapphire are both forms of corundum.

cove *noun*
A cove is a small bay or inlet on the coast, which is sheltered by **headlands**. A cove is often rocky at the sides. It may have a sandy beach in the centre.
The geologist discovered some unusual rocks on the beach of the cove.

crag *noun*
A crag is a steep rock sticking out from the side of a hill or a mountain. Some crags are made when **weathering** erodes the rock of a mountain.
The rock climbers saw many crags as they explored the mountains.

crater *noun*
A crater is a hollow on the surface of a planet. Craters are circular in shape and have steep sides. They can be made by **meteorites** which crash into the planet. The mouth of a volcano is also called a crater.
There was smoke rising from the crater of the volcano.

creek *noun*
A creek is a narrow, winding **channel** with a stream at the bottom. Creeks are often found in muddy areas, such as **salt-marshes**. Many creeks are flooded by the sea at high tide.
We jumped over the creek and walked across the marsh.

crest *noun*
A crest is the top of a hill or a mountain. From the crest of a hill, it is often possible to see down into the valleys on both sides.
We kept on walking upwards until we reached the crest of the hill.

Cretaceous *adjective*
Cretaceous describes a **period** in **geological time**. The Cretaceous Period lasted from about 144 million years ago to about 65 million years ago.
The dinosaurs became extinct during the Cretaceous Period.

crevasse *noun*
A crevasse is a deep, steep-sided hole in the ice of an **ice-field** or **glacier**. Crevasses are formed when the ice moves and splits. A crevasse can be hundreds of metres deep.
We turned back because we could not cross the crevasse safely.

crude oil *noun*
Crude oil is the name used for petroleum when it first comes out of the ground. Oil wells pump crude oil from **oilfields** deep under the ground or from under the sea. Crude oil is a heavy, brown liquid. It is refined to make many **petroleum** products.
The earth around the well was stained brown with crude oil.

crust *noun*
The crust is the outermost part of the **Earth**. The **continental crust** is about 35 kilometres thick below the surface of the land. The **oceanic crust** is about 5 kilometres thick under the sea. The crust is made up mostly of **granite** and **basalt**.
The whole of the Earth's surface is covered by a crust.

crystal ▶ page 37

crystallize *verb*
Crystallize describes the way in which non-living, or **inorganic**, matter grows into **crystals**. Gases, liquids or solids may crystallize. Some substances crystallize if they lose all their water. Others crystallize if they become very cold.
The water crystallized into ice in the freezing weather.

continent *noun*

A continent is a large **land mass**. It is formed from **continental crust**, and rises steeply from the **ocean floor**. A continent contains a wide range of geological and geographical **features**. There are seven continents. These are Asia, Africa, North America, South America, Antarctica, Europe and Australia. Asia is the largest continent.

The continent of North American stretches from the Atlantic Ocean to the Pacific Ocean.

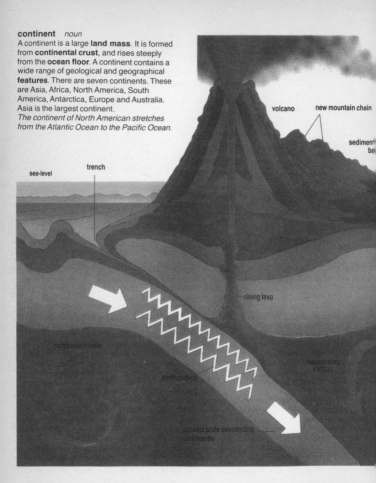

volcano

new mountain chain

sediment bar

sea-level

trench

rising lava

subduction zone

descending current

earthquakes

oceanic plate descending into mantle

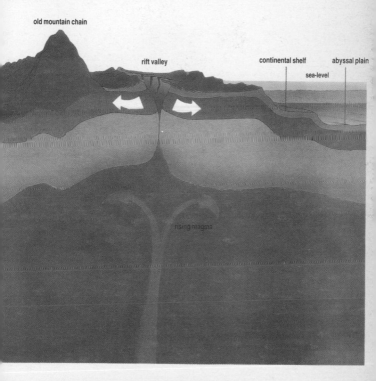

old mountain chain

rift valley

continental shelf

abyssal plain

sea-level

rising magma

crystallography *noun*
Crystallography is the study of **crystals**.
It looks at the outer shape of crystals and
also at their inner structure.
*The scientist used crystallography to discover
the way the mineral was made.*

cumulonimbus *adjective*
Cumulonimbus describes a kind of **cloud**.
A cumulonimbus cloud is very tall and is a grey
colour. It often spreads out at the top.
Cumulonimbus clouds bring heavy showers
and storms.
*We saw cumulonimbus clouds gathering
before the storm.*

cumulus *adjective*
Cumulus describes a kind of **cloud**. Cumulus
clouds look rounded and fluffy and can be
very tall. They often develop in **convection
currents** of warm air, particularly in hot
weather.
*The large cumulus clouds moved slowly
across the sky.*

current *noun*
A current is a movement of air or water. In the
sea, currents are caused by the rotation of the
Earth and by the winds. In the **northern
hemisphere**, the main ocean currents flow in
a clockwise direction. In the **southern
hemisphere**, they move in an anticlockwise
direction. Air currents are caused by
convection.
*The Gulf Stream is the main current in the
north Atlantic Ocean.*

cycle *noun*
A cycle is a process in which any material
moves round a system. Water moves in a
cycle from the sea into the air by
evaporation, and then falls as rain or snow
onto the land. The water cycle is completed
when the water gathers in rivers and flows to
the sea.
*Rainfall is an important part of the water
cycle.*

cyclone *noun*
A cyclone is a very strong wind. Cyclones
sometimes blow around an area of low
atmospheric pressure, particularly in the
tropics. Cyclone is sometimes used as
another name for a **depression**.
*The strong cyclone destroyed houses and
brought flooding.*

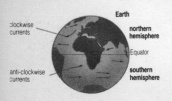

clockwise currents

Earth

northern hemisphere

Equator

anti-clockwise currents

southern hemisphere

crystal *noun*

A crystal is a solid with a regular shape, such as cubic or tetragonal. Crystals are often hard and shiny, and have smooth, flat surfaces. Most **minerals** are found naturally as crystals.

Grains of common salt and precious stones, such as diamonds, are crystals.

monoclinic shape

natural gypsum

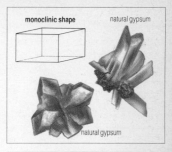

natural gypsum

cubic shape

natural garnet

pyrite

cut garnet

tetragonal shape

natural zircon

cut zircon

natural zircon

triclinic shape

natural feldspar

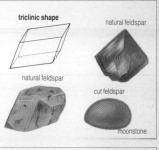

natural feldspar

cut feldspar

moonstone

orthorhombic shape

natural topaz

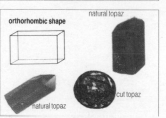

natural topaz

cut topaz

hexagonal shape

natural quartz

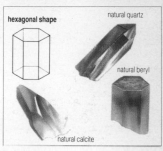

natural beryl

natural calcite

D

dam *noun*
A dam is a structure which controls the flow of water. Dams are built to hold water in **reservoirs**, or to stop flooding.
The valley flooded when the dam burst.

reservoir

dam

decay *verb*
Decay is a word which describes the gradual change of **radioactive** material. Radioactive **elements**, such as **uranium** and **radium**, set particles of radioactivity free as they decay. Decay is also used to describe how dead things rot and break down.
The amount of the radioactive element decreased as it decayed.

decompose *verb*
Decompose describes the breaking up of a **chemical** into simpler material. When animals and plants die, the complicated **organic** substances of their bodies decompose into simpler substances in the ground.
The dead trees gradually decomposed and became part of the soil.
decomposition *noun*

deep-sea plain ▶ **abyssal plain**

degree *noun*
A degree is a unit used for measuring **temperature**. The two common scales for temperature are **Celsius**, or centigrade, and **Fahrenheit**. A degree is also the unit for measuring direction on a **compass** and in lines of **latitude** and **longitude**.
Pure water boils at 100 degrees on the Celsius scale.

delta *noun*
A delta is the wide, fan-shaped part of a **river** where it flows into a lake or the sea. The delta is made by the **sediment** which is carried by the river water. As the river water meets the water of a lake or the sea, the sediment is deposited on the ground. River deltas can spread out over a large area.
The land in a delta is muddy and very fertile.

deposit *noun*
A deposit is any material which is laid down. The water in a river leaves a deposit, or **sediment**, of gravel and mud on the river bed.
The water left a deposit of chalk in the kettle.

depression *noun*
A depression is an area where the **atmospheric pressure** is low. Depressions bring cloudy skies, unsettled weather and often rain. The opposite of a depression, or **cyclone**, is an **anticyclone**. Depression is also the word for a **hollow** in the ground.
As the depression arrived, it began to rain steadily.

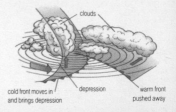

clouds

cold front moves in and brings depression

depression

warm front pushed away

desalination   *noun*
Desalination is the way salt is removed from a substance, especially sea water. Desalination takes the salt out of sea water to make it suitable for drinking.
Most of the drinking water in Saudi Arabia is produced by desalination.

desert   *noun*
A desert is a dry, open area of land. Deserts usually have less than 25 centimetres of rain a year. A heavier rainfall that **evaporates** quickly may also occur in a desert. Some deserts, like the Sahara in North Africa, are hot. Other deserts are cold, like the Gobi in eastern Asia. A much smaller range of plants and animals is found in deserts than in other areas. But many kinds of plant and animal are able to live in deserts.
The polar deserts of the Arctic and Antarctica are covered in snow and ice.

desertification   *noun*
Desertification describes how a **desert** spreads. If there are too many animals living in an area, they will eat all the grass and plants. Without the plants to protect it, the soil will suffer from **erosion** and become infertile.
Desertification is increasing the size of the Sahara in North Africa.

detritus   *noun*
Detritus is loose, rocky material produced by the **weathering** of exposed rock. Detritus is washed away by rivers and rain and gathers at the bottom of seas, rivers and lakes, as well as on land.
There was a thick layer of detritus at the edge of the cliff.

Devonian   *adjective*
Devonian describes a **period** in **geological time**. The Devonian Period lasted from about 408 million years ago to 360 million years ago and was part of the **Paleozoic** Era.
Animals with backbones first came on to the land during the Devonian Period.

dew   *noun*
Dew is a collection of water droplets. The droplets **condense** from the water vapour in the air on to the ground, or on to plants. Dew forms at night, when the air cools to below the **dew point**.
In the early morning, the grass was wet with dew.

dew point   *noun*
The dew point is the temperature at which **dew** forms from the air. The dew point depends on the dampness of the air and on the **atmospheric pressure**.
The grass became wet as the air cooled and the dew point was reached.

diamond   *noun*
Diamond is a shiny, transparent **crystal**. It is a form of **carbon** and is the hardest natural substance known. Colourless diamonds are cut into **gems** for jewellery.
She scratched her name on the glass with the diamond in her ring.

dinosaur   *noun*
A dinosaur is any one of a group of reptiles which lived during the **Mesozoic** Era. Dinosaurs died out at the end of the **Cretaceous** Period.
Many dinosaurs walked on two legs.

Ouranosaurus

doldrums   *noun*
The doldrums describes an area of the **oceans** where the **winds** are often very weak. The doldrums lie a little way north and south of the **Equator**, between the **trade winds**.
Sailing boats sometimes get stuck in the calm weather of the doldrums.

dolerite *noun*
Dolerite is a kind of **igneous** rock. It is a dark colour and contains large amounts of **feldspar**. Dolerite is common all over the world.
The geologist found that the rocks were made of dolerite.

dolomite *noun*
Dolomite is a **mineral**. It is a **compound** called calcium magnesium carbonate. Dolomite is one of the chief sources of **magnesium**. One kind of **sedimentary** rock, which contains calcium magnesium carbonate, is also called dolomite. Many mountain ranges, especially in Europe, have huge amounts of dolomite rock.
Weathering has worn the dolomite rock into jagged cliffs and peaks.

dome *noun*
A dome is a kind of **anticline** in which all the sides slope away evenly from a central point. Domes may be many kilometres in diameter, or small with steep sides. A dome of impervious rock may act as a trap for **oil** and **natural gas**. A dome can also describe a **hill** with smooth sides. The opposite of a dome is a **basin**.
It was easy to walk up the dome because the slope was so gentle.

dormant *adjective*
Dormant describes a **volcano** which has not erupted recently, but which might erupt in the future.
On May 18th 1980, the dormant volcano of Mount St Helens erupted in the United States of America.

drainage *noun*
Drainage describes the way water runs away through the soil. If a soil has good drainage, it will dry out quickly after rain. Soil with bad drainage quickly becomes full of water and is difficult to use.
He improved the drainage by digging a ditch below the field.

drought *noun*
A drought is a long period without rain. Wild plants and animals can often survive short droughts, but crops may suffer badly.
Some areas, such as deserts, often suffer from droughts.

dune *noun*
A dune is a large hill of **sand**. The sand is shaped and moved by the wind. Dunes take two main forms, a half-moon or crescent shape, and a narrow ridge shape. Long lines of dunes cover large areas of sand **deserts**. Dunes are also found near the sea, behind sandy beaches.
We found it difficult to walk over the soft dunes.

dust *noun*
Dust is a collection of powdery particles of **earth**. In dry weather, dust covers the surface of the soil and finds its way into every hole and corner.
The dust was very fine and was easily blown by the wind.

dust bowl *noun*
The dust bowl is a part of the central plains of the United States of America. The dust bowl includes the states of Kansas and Texas. It sometimes has **dust storms**.
In the 1930s, dry weather and storms destroyed much of the farmland of the dust bowl.

dust devil *noun*

A dust devil is a small, circular column of **wind** which has picked up **dust** and soil. It is a kind of small **tornado** which occurs in dry areas. A dust devil can move quite quickly, at a speed of up to 30 kilometres per hour.
The dust devils looked like moving towers of smoke.

dust storm *noun*

A dust storm is a strong wind which picks up and carries **dust**. Dust storms take place mostly in areas with a hot climate, especially where the soil is fine and dry. Sometimes, small **tornados** pick up dust and become dust storms.
They could no longer see the fields when the dust storm arrived.

Earth ▶ page 42

earth *noun*

Earth is another name for **soil**. Earth is the loose material lying above rocks. It is made of tiny pieces of rock, dust and sand. These pieces are mixed with **organic** material which has decomposed.
Plants grow by rooting themselves into the earth.

Earth science *noun*

Earth science is the study of the Earth, including the **oceans** and the **atmosphere**. Geology, **meteorology**, glaciology and **oceanography** are all parts of Earth science.
She studied Earth science to help her understand what happens in the oceans.

earthquake ▶ page 46

ebb *verb*

Ebb describes the outward movement of the **tide**. When the tide ebbs, the water in the sea or in an **estuary** moves away from the land. The opposite of ebb is **flow**.
The boat floated out as the tide began to ebb.

echo sounder *noun*

An echo sounder measures the distance of something under water. It sends out sound waves, which bounce back off the sea-bed, the river bed or an object under water. The echo sounder calculates depth or distance by measuring the time between sending the sound waves and receiving the echo.
Some fishing boats have echo sounders to help find shoals of fish.

Earth *noun*

The Earth is the world on which we live.
The Earth is made up of several parts. In the
centre is the **inner core**, which is very dense
and may be solid. Round the inner core is the
outer core, which may be liquid. Both parts of
the core are probably made of an alloy of iron
and nickel. The third layer is the **mantle**.
This is formed from molten rocks. Above the
mantle is the **crust**, or **lithosphere**. The outer
surface of the crust is covered by land
masses such as **continents**, and by **oceans**.
Beyond the crust is the **atmosphere**.
The Earth is made up of many different
materials.

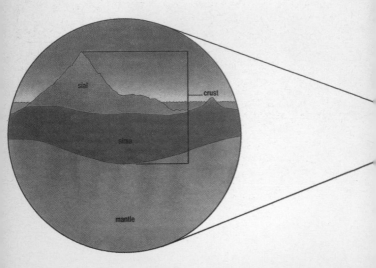

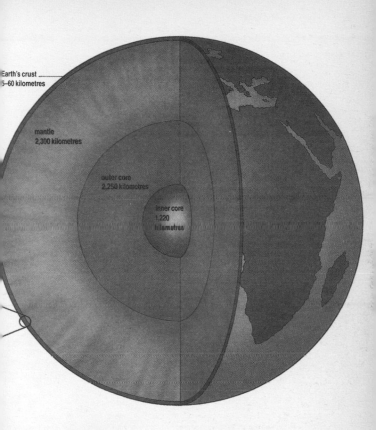

Earth's crust
5–60 kilometres

mantle
2,300 kilometres

outer core
2,250 kilometres

inner core
1,220
kilometres

element *noun*
An element is a simple substance. An element cannot be changed by chemical reaction into any simpler substance. **Carbon**, **hydrogen** and **oxygen** are all examples of elements. Elements join together to form **compounds**. Scientists know of just over 100 different elements so far.
Platinum is a very rare element.

elevation *noun*
Elevation describes the height of an object. Elevation is usually measured in metres above **sea-level**.
The mountain hut was at an elevation of 2,000 metres.

emerald *noun*
Emerald is a green, transparent **crystal**. It is a kind of **beryl**, which contains traces of **chromium**. It is a precious stone.
Emeralds are often used in jewellery.

emery *noun*
Emery is a hard **mineral** which is found in rocks. It is a mixture of **corundum** and oxides of **iron**. Emery is used as an **abrasive** to polish stones.
The paper had small pieces of emery stuck on its surface, like sandpaper.

energy *noun*
Energy is the ability to do work. There are different kinds of energy, including heat energy, light energy, movement or kinetic energy, and chemical energy. Each kind of energy can be changed into another kind.
The waves in the sea contain large amounts of energy.

environment *noun*
Environment is a word which describes our surroundings, or the surroundings of an animal or plant. The environment includes the other animals and plants nearby, as well as the soil, rocks, water and **climate**.
They changed the environment of the rain forest by cutting down the trees.

Eocene *adjective*
Eocene is the name of an **epoch** in **geological time**. The Eocene Epoch occurred in the **Tertiary** sub-era and lasted from about 55 million years ago to about 38 million years ago.
The mountains of the Himalayas were formed in the Eocene Epoch.

eon *noun*
An eon is one of the divisions of **geological time**. There are four eons, each covering a very long period of time. The Phanerozoic Eon is the most recent. It is divided into **eras**, **periods** and **epochs**.
Most forms of life have developed during the Phanerozoic Eon.

epicentre *noun*
The epicentre is the point on the Earth's surface directly above the centre, or **focus**, of an **earthquake**. The strongest effects of an earthquake are usually felt at its epicentre.
The city was destroyed because it was on the epicentre of the earthquake.

epoch *noun*
An epoch is one of the divisions of **geological time**. It is a small part of a larger division called a **period**.
We live today in the Holocene Epoch.

Equator *noun*
The Equator is an imaginary line which is drawn around the **globe**. **Latitudes** are measured to the north and south of the Equator, which has latitude 0 degrees. The Equator divides the Earth into two halves, the northern and southern **hemispheres**.
The passengers gave a cheer as the boat crossed the Equator.

Earth Equator

44

equatorial *adjective*
Equatorial describes something which is found near the **Equator**. The equatorial rain forests grow in this region, and the equatorial **current** flows in the seas near the Equator.
The climate is hot in equatorial countries.

era *noun*
An era is one of the main divisions of **geological time**. Each era is divided into **periods**. The order of eras from oldest to youngest is **Paleozoic**, **Mesozoic** and **Cenozoic**.
The dinosaurs lived in the Mesozoic Era.

erg *noun*
An erg is a large area of sand which may be flat or may form sand **dunes**. Ergs are found in deserts and can cover huge areas, especially in the Sahara in North Africa.
The camel caravan crossed the erg.

erode *verb*
To erode is to wear away the surface of something. The wind, water and ice are constantly eroding the rocks and soils of the Earth.
The rock face was eroded by the wind and rain.

erosion ▶ page 49

erupt *verb*
Erupt describes how a **volcano** explodes. Some volcanoes do not erupt for many years, or even centuries. Other volcanoes erupt more frequently.
We dared not go too near the volcano, in case it erupted.

eruption *noun*
An eruption is the explosion of a **volcano**. In an eruption, a volcano spouts out ash and red-hot **lava**, which flows down the sides of the volcano.
After the eruption, every living thing on the sides of the volcano was burned.

escarpment *noun*
An escarpment is a steep slope rising up from a **plain**. An escarpment is formed when the rocks are **eroded** much more quickly at one side of a hill than at the other.
The escarpment blocked the route out of the valley.

layers of rock escarpment

esker *noun*
An esker is a long, narrow hill or **ridge**, winding along a **valley** floor. Eskers are created by streams flowing underneath **glaciers**. The streams leave behind **sand** and **gravel**, which form the esker.
The road followed the top of the esker.

estuary *noun*
An estuary is the part of a **river** where fresh water flows into the sea. The fresh river water mixes with the salty sea water. An estuary is affected by the **tides**. The water in the parts of the river nearest the sea rises and falls as the tide **ebbs** and **flows**.
Many seaports are built on estuaries.

earthquake *noun*

An earthquake is a large, sudden movement
of the Earth's **crust**. The crust is divided into
several **tectonic plates**. The edges of the
plates are marked by **faults**. When the plates
move past each other, or collide, earthquakes
can occur along the fault lines. The strength of
an earthquake is measured on the
Richter Scale.

*Strong earthquakes may cause great damage
and loss of life.*

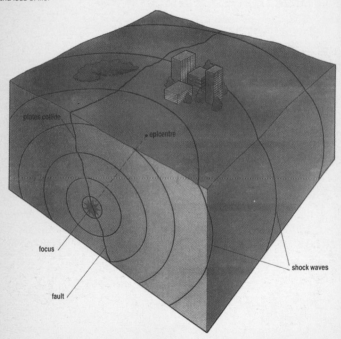

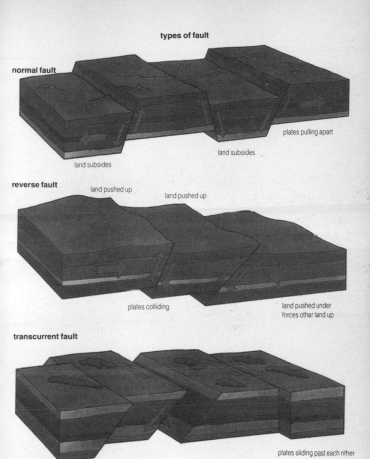

types of fault

normal fault

plates pulling apart

land subsides

land subsides

land subsides

reverse fault

land pushed up

land pushed up

plates colliding

land pushed under
forces other land up

transcurrent fault

plates sliding past each other

evaporate   *verb*
Evaporate is a word which describes how a liquid changes into a **gas** or **vapour**. When water evaporates, it turns from a liquid into water **vapour** in the air. Water evaporates when it is heated.
The water in the bowl evaporated in the heat of the Sun.

evaporation   *noun*
Evaporation describes what happens when a liquid turns into a **gas**. Water turns into water **vapour** in the air when it evaporates from the soil and from the sea.
The level of water in the small lake went down because of evaporation.

excavate   *verb*
To excavate is to dig carefully into the ground in order to find something. Geologists excavate **quarries** and **cliffs** when looking for **fossils** or different rocks.
The team excavated the ground to uncover the dinosaur bones.

excavation   *noun*

extinct   *adjective*
Extinct describes a **volcano** which has not **erupted** for a long time and which is not expected to erupt again. The opposite of an extinct volcano is an **active** volcano. Extinct also describes an **organism** which is no longer living.
The extinct volcano was covered with trees.

extract   *verb*
To extract something is to take it out. **Metals** are extracted from their **ores** by melting or by the use of **chemicals**.
They extracted pure gold from the rocks.

extraction   *noun*
Extraction describes how one substance is taken out of a mixture. Extraction can be done by heating and melting the mixture, or by dissolving the mixture in **chemicals**.
Metals are taken from their ores by the process of extraction.

extreme   *adjective*
An extreme **temperature** is a very hot or a very cold temperature. Extreme describes something which is beyond the usual range that is known to us.
They were forced to shelter from the extreme heat of the desert.

eye   *noun*
Eye is sometimes used to describe the central part of a storm of circular winds or **hurricane**. The air in the area of the eye is calm.
The eye of the storm was surrounded by fierce, swirling winds.

erosion *noun*

Erosion is the wearing down of **rocks** or
soils. Erosion is caused by the action of
water, **wind** or **ice**, or by living organisms.
The force of sea water washing against cliffs
will erode the cliffs, breaking down the solid
rock into smaller pieces. Further erosion will
turn boulders and pebbles into sand. Many
interesting **rock formations** and **features** are
caused by erosion.

*The headlands at each end of the bay were
eroded by the sea into a range of sea cliffs.*

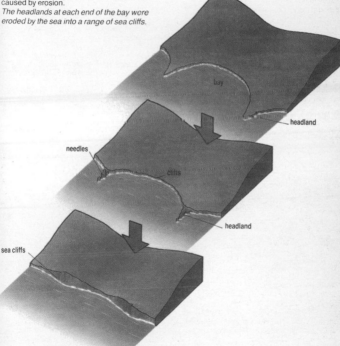

bay

headland

needles

cliffs

headland

sea cliffs

F

facet *noun*

A facet is part of a precious stone or **gem**. A gem used for jewellery is cut into several flat surfaces. Each of these flat surfaces is called a facet.

Each facet of the diamond shone.

facet —

Fahrenheit *noun*

Fahrenheit is a scale used for measuring **temperature**. On the Fahrenheit scale, the freezing point of water is 32 degrees and the boiling point is 212 degrees.

The daily temperature is measured on the Fahrenheit scale in the United States of America.

fault *noun*

A fault is a crack in rocks, caused by movements of the Earth's **crust**. Faults can make the ground crack and bend. Sometimes, **valleys** and **cliffs** are created by faults.

One of the most famous faults is the San Andreas Fault in California, in the United States of America.

feature ► page 52

feldspar *noun*

Feldspar is a kind of **mineral**. Feldspar is made up of **crystals**. It contains **aluminium** and **silica**, with mixtures of **sodium**, **potassium** and **calcium**.

Nearly half of all the rocks in the Earth's crust are feldspar.

fen *noun*

A fen is a kind of wetland. In a fen, the water has a high **mineral** content, and the main plants are sedges and grasses. Fens often develop at the edges of **lowland** lakes.

We found it difficult to walk over the fen without getting our feet wet.

ferrous *adjective*

Ferrous describes something that is made of the metal **iron**, or that contains iron. A ferrous metal is a metal which contains a large amount of iron.

Steel is an example of a ferrous metal.

fertile *adjective*

Fertile describes something that can support growth. Healthy plants grow in a fertile soil. Fertile also describes an animal or plant which can produce young or seeds.

The farmer grew good crops in the fertile soil.

fertilizer *noun*

Fertilizer is a **chemical** or mixture of chemicals added to soil to make it more **fertile**. Compost and manure are forms of natural fertilizer.

Most fertilizers contain nitrogen.

fissure *noun*

A fissure is a cleft or crack in a rock or in the soil. A fissure is long and narrow. Fissures happen when the ground splits or when rock is worn away by water. They are common in **volcanic** areas.

We could see the steam rising from the fissure in the rock.

fjord *noun*

A fjord is a deep **inlet** of the sea with steep mountain slopes on each side. Fjords are found on hilly or mountainous **coasts**. They were formed when the sea flooded river valleys caused by glaciers.
The coasts of Norway and of the South Island of New Zealand have many fjords.

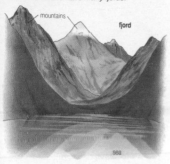

flash flood *noun*

A flash flood is a **flood** which happens very suddenly. Flash floods occur mainly in warm countries, especially where the rocks are **impervious** and water cannot soak away. They can destroy crops and cause **erosion**.
The flash flood washed away the soil.

flint *noun*

Flint is a hard rock. It is found as grey or brown **pebbles** in **chalk** or **limestone**.
In the Stone Age, people made tools by breaking the flint into pieces.

flood *noun*

A flood is a sudden rise in **water level**. It covers land that is usually dry. Floods may happen on low-lying land near the **coast** when there are high **tides** and strong winds.
Heavy rainfall can cause a flood by raising the water level of a river over its banks.

flood plain *noun*

A flood plain is the flat valley floor which fills with water when a **lowland** river floods. A flood plain usually has very **fertile** soil made of **sediment** dropped by the river when it floods.
The river flowed in many meanders along the flood plain.

flora *noun*

Flora is the word used for all of the plants of a particular region or a particular time. The **tropical rain forests** have the richest flora on Earth.
The flora of the Arctic is very poor.

flow *verb*

Flow describes the inward movement of the **tide**. When the tide flows, the water in the sea or in an **estuary** moves towards the land. The opposite of flow is **ebb**.
The boat had to wait until the tide began to flow before it could sail.

fluorine *noun*

Fluorine is an **element**. It is a yellow **gas** which is found naturally in the mineral **fluorite**. Sodium fluoride is a fluorine **compound** which is sometimes added to drinking water. It helps teeth to grow strong.
Fluorine forms compounds with nearly all other elements.

fluorite *noun*

Fluorite is a **mineral**. It has a white or purple colour. Fluorite is made of calcium fluoride and is the main source of **fluorine**. Fluorite is found mainly in mineral **veins**.
The scientists found fluorite in the floor of the quarry.

feature *noun*

A feature is a part of the **landscape** that stands out. In a flat **plain**, a steep **cliff** is a feature in the landscape. Some features, such as the ones below, are so unusual that they are famous all over the world.

The huge rock formations were the main feature of the valley.

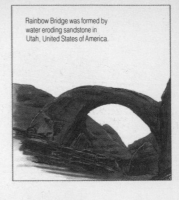

Rainbow Bridge was formed by water eroding sandstone in Utah, United States of America.

Strange piles of rock can sometimes be found in the ergs in the Sahara in North Africa.

Houses have been built into these volcanic rock formations in Cappadocia, Turkey.

This red sandstone butte is in Monument Valley in Utah, United States of America.

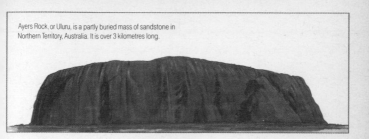

Ayers Rock, or Uluru, is a partly buried mass of sandstone in Northern Territory, Australia. It is over 3 kilometres long.

These limestone rock formations are in the Band-i-Amir river in the Hindu Kush mountains of Afghanistan.

These six-sided basalt columns are part of the Giant's Causeway in County Antrim, Northern Ireland.

focus *noun*
The focus is the point below the Earth's surface where an **earthquake** begins. The point on the surface of the Earth directly above the focus is called the **epicentre** of the earthquake.
The focus of the earthquake was deep below the Earth's surface.

fog *noun*
Fog is the word used when thick **clouds** form at ground level. Fog develops when water **vapour** in the air cools below the **dew point**.
The fog was so thick that they could not see the road ahead.

fold *noun*
A fold is a bend in a layer of rocks. Folds are found most commonly in **sedimentary** and **metamorphic** rocks. A fold which is arch-shaped is called an **anticline**. A fold which is trough-shaped is a **syncline**.
The coloured bands in the rock showed the fold very clearly.

syncline | anticline | fold | layers of rock

fold mountain *noun*
A fold mountain is a mountain which was formed from a **fold** in the rocks. The mountains of Scotland, Wales and Norway are fold mountains, and so are the Himalayas in Asia and the Pyrenees in Europe.
We could see the long chain of fold mountains stretching into the distance.

ford *noun*
A ford is the place where a road crosses a **stream** or a **river**. The water is usually shallow and the bed of the river is firm.
We walked beside the stream until we could cross it at the ford.

forecast *noun*
A forecast tells people about what might happen in the future. The **weather forecast** gives information about future weather. The shipping forecast gives the weather at sea.
He listened to the weather forecast before setting out.

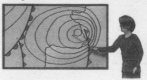

foreshock *noun*
Foreshock is the name given to a shock or **tremor** which occurs a short time before an **earthquake**. The earthquake may be followed by an **aftershock**.
The foreshock came before the earthquake.

forest *noun*
A forest is a large area of woodland. Many forests grow naturally and may be hundreds of years old. Some forests are carefully planted and the wood is cut at intervals. This wood is a **natural resource**.
In northern Europe, dark, coniferous forests stretch for hundreds of kilometres.

forestry *noun*
Forestry is the study and care of growing and developing **forests**. Someone who practises forestry is called a forester. A forester may look after trees being grown especially for timber, as well as caring for natural forests.
Forestry kept the beech trees healthy.

fossil ► page 56

fossil fuel *noun*
Fossil fuel is fuel formed from the fossilized remains of plants. **Peat**, **coal** and **natural gas** are all fossil fuels. Fossil fuels contain **carbon** and are a good source of **energy** when burned.
Fossil fuels will not last for ever.

fracture *noun*
A fracture is an area in the Earth's surface where the rocks have moved apart. Many fractures are found beside the **mid-oceanic ridges** at the bottom of the sea.
The fracture in the rocks was caused by an earthquake.

freeze-thaw *adjective*
Freeze-thaw describes a kind of **weathering**. In freeze-thaw weathering, the water in rocks or soils freezes and then thaws repeatedly. Water expands when it freezes, so it enlarges any cracks in the rocks. Freeze-thaw action is most common during cold weather in high mountains, and in the **polar** regions.
The rocks were covered in tiny cracks caused by freeze-thaw action.

fresh water *noun*
Fresh water is the water usually found in the ground and in rivers and lakes. Unlike sea water, fresh water does not have a high salt ꞇꞔꞔꞔꞔꞔꞔ and is usually turned into drinking water.
At the top of an estuary, the water changes from salt water to fresh water.

front *noun*
A front describes a sharp change in the **temperature** of air. A **warm front** occurs at the edge of a mass of warm air and a **cold front** is found at the edge of a mass of cold air. Fronts also separate water masses of different temperatures in the **ocean**.
The weather suddenly became milder as the warm front arrived.

frontier *noun*
A frontier is an imaginary line which separates one country from another. The frontier is also the part of a country that faces, or fronts, another country. Some frontiers are marked by a fence or a wall. Some are formed by natural barriers, such as mountains or rivers.
They crossed the frontier between Pakistan and India by train.

frost *noun*
Frost occurs when the air or ground **temperature** is so cold that **ice** forms. Moisture in the air or on the ground **condenses** and then freezes on the soil and on plants.
A severe frost can kill delicate kinds of plants.

fuel *noun*
Fuel is any substance which is used to produce **energy**. **Coal**, **gas** and **oil** are fuels which are burned to obtain heat. Petroleum is another fuel, which is made from **crude oil**. Nuclear power stations use **radioactive chemicals** as fuel, usually a form of **uranium**.
The crude oil was used to make fuel.

fumarole *noun*
A fumarole is a small hole in the Earth's surface through which steam and **gases** escape. Fumaroles are found in **volcanic** areas. The steam comes from water heated by **magma** under the ground. **Dormant** volcanoes sometimes have many fumaroles.
We watched the hot steam rising out of the fumarole.

funnel *noun*
A funnel is an opening in rocks, which is wide at the top and narrow at the bottom.
The funnel in the rocks had been caused by erosion.

fossil *noun*

A fossil is the remains of an organism that lived on Earth in an earlier **geological time**. Fossils are usually found in **sedimentary** rocks. The study of fossils is called **paleontology**.

They found the fossil of an ammonite in the limestone.

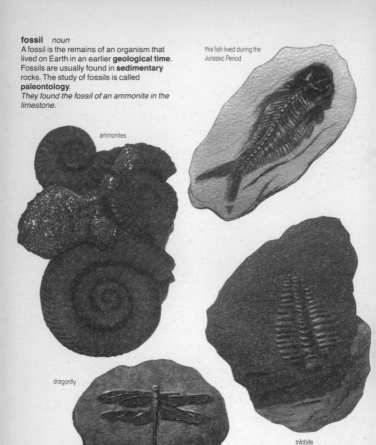

this fish lived during the Jurassic Period

ammonites

dragonfly

trilobite

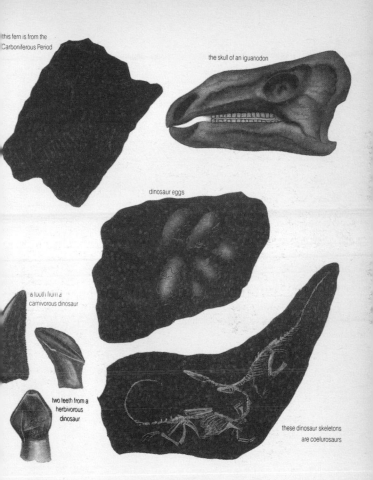

this fern is from the Carboniferous Period

the skull of an iguanodon

dinosaur eggs

a tooth from a carnivorous dinosaur

two teeth from a herbivorous dinosaur

these dinosaur skeletons are coelurosaurs

G

gale *noun*
A gale is a very strong **wind**. A gale breaks twigs from trees. A strong gale can damage buildings. A gale measures between forces 7 and 9 on the **Beaufort Scale**.
The gale blew so hard that we found it difficult to walk upright.

galena *noun*
Galena is a **mineral**. Galena is made of dark grey crystals of **lead** sulphide. Galena is the most important source of the metal lead.
The miners found large deposits of galena in the rocks.

garnet *noun*
Garnet is the name used for a group of **minerals** found mostly in **metamorphic** rocks. Garnet crystals are made of **silicates** of **magnesium**, **aluminium**, **iron** and **calcium**. Dark red garnets are used as **gems**.
A garnet can be used as an abrasive.

gas *noun*
A gas is a substance. The molecules in a gas are very active and are well spread out. Gases have low densities and can be compressed. They can also flow freely.
Air is a mixture of gases, mostly nitrogen and oxygen.

gaseous *adjective*
Gaseous is the word used to describe a substance when it is a **gas**. All substances change to a gaseous form when they reach a high enough **temperature**.
Water vapour is the gaseous form of water.

gem ▶ page 60

geo- *prefix*
Geo- is a prefix used to refer to the **Earth**.
We learn about the Earth's rocks and minerals in geology.

geochemistry *noun*
Geochemistry is the study of the chemical **elements** that are found on **Earth**. It includes studying the chemical processes involved in the Earth's history.
The study of geochemistry helps scientists to find mineral deposits.

geode *noun*
A geode is a hole completely surrounded by rock. Geodes are found in **igneous** rocks. They are partly filled by mineral **crystals**.
The geologist found a patch of shiny crystals hidden inside the geode.

geodesy *noun*
Geodesy is the study of the size and shape of the **Earth** and its field of **gravity**. In geodesy, scientists measure the curve of the Earth.
He learned about the shape of the Earth by studying geodesy.

geographer *noun*
A geographer is someone who studies or practises **geography**.
The geographer described the continents of the Earth to us.

geography *noun*
Geography is the study of the **Earth's**
surface. Physical geography includes the
Earth's **climate**, **vegetation** and **oceans**.
Human geography looks at the peoples of the
world and their **environments**. Mathematical
geography studies the size, shape and
movements of the Earth.
*We learned about the main features of the
countryside in geography.*

geological time ▶ page 64

geologist *noun*
A geologist is someone who studies or
practises **geology**.
*The geologist studied the rocks and minerals
of the cliff.*

geology *noun*
Geology is the study of the **Earth**. Different
branches of geology deal with the Earth's
history, the movements that take place within
it, the materials it is made from and the
shapes of these materials. Geology also
studies the plants and animals that have lived
on Earth throughout the different ages.
*We knew the age of the fossils by studying the
geology of the rocks from which they came.*

geomagnetism *noun*
Geomagnetism is the **magnetism** of the
Earth. It is caused by the metals at the **core**
of the Earth, which act like a huge **magnet**.
These metals, which are mainly **iron** and
nickel, set up a **magnetic field** around the
Earth.
*The needle of her compass moved because
of geomagnetism.*

geomorphology *noun*
Geomorphology is a branch of **geology**.
It studies the structure of the **Earth's** surface.
Geomorphology looks at changes such as
erosion and the laying down of **deposits**.
*His knowledge of geomorphology helped him
to discover how long it had taken the rocks to
wear away.*

geophysics *noun*
Geophysics is a branch of **geology**.
Geophysics looks at the physical properties of
the **Earth** and at the forces which shape it.
*The study of the Earth's magnetic field is a
part of geophysics.*

geothermal energy *noun*
Geothermal energy is **energy** which comes
from the heat of the Earth's rocks. In some
areas, geothermal energy is used for heating
water and for making electricity.
*Every room in the house was heated by
geothermal energy.*

geyser *noun*
A geyser is a fountain of hot water and steam
found in **volcanic** areas. Geysers only spout
at intervals, when hot water and **gases** build
up underground.
*The world's most famous geyser is Old
Faithful in the Yellowstone National Park,
in the United States of America.*

glaciation *noun*
Glaciation is the way in which land is shaped
by **ice**. Thick layers of ice move slowly over
hills and mountains. The ice gouges out the
soil and rocks. Glaciation is also the name for
the times in geological history when ice
covered the Earth.
*The sides of the valley had been worn smooth
during the last glaciation.*

glacier ▶ page 66

gem *noun*

A gem is any precious or semi-precious
mineral. Gems may be many different
colours, including red rubies, green emeralds,
or blue sapphires.
Most gems and crystals are very shiny.

uncut peridot

cut peridot

uncut garnet

cut garnet

cut jade

uncut jade

uncut diamond

cut diamond

uncut amber

cut amber

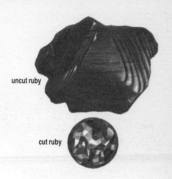

uncut ruby

cut ruby

uncut turquoise

cut turquoise

uncut sapphire

cut sapphire

glass *noun*
Glass is a clear substance made from **lime**, soda and **silica**. Glass turns liquid when it is heated. Liquid glass can be moulded or blown into different shapes. Elements, such as **boron** and **lead**, are added to glass to give it special properties. Glass occurs naturally as **obsidian**.
We could see the fish clearly through the glass at the side of the tank.

global *adjective*
Global describes something which affects the whole **Earth**. An animal or plant that is found throughout the world has a global distribution. Global warming heats up the **climate** of the whole Earth.
The astronauts had a global view of Earth from their spacecraft.

globe *noun*
The globe is the name given to the planet **Earth**.
The spacecraft circled the globe.

gneiss *noun*
Gneiss is a kind of **metamorphic** rock. It is made up of coarse **crystals** arranged in light and dark coloured bands. The largest areas of gneiss in the world are in central Australia, in Canada and in the Baltic region of northern Europe.
The rocks of the hill were made of gneiss.

gold *noun*
Gold is an **element**. It is a soft, bright yellow **metal**. Gold is rare and valuable and does not react easily with other **chemicals**.
Gold is used for making some coins, jewellery and ornaments.

Gondwanaland *noun*
Gondwanaland is the name of a large **continent** which no longer exists. Some scientists think that it formed when **Pangaea** split up about 215 million years ago, during the **Mesozoic** Era. Gondwanaland may also have split, to create South America, Antarctica, Africa, India, Australia and New Zealand.
Some scientists think Gondwanaland was to be found in the southern hemisphere.

gorge *noun*
A gorge is a very deep **valley** with steep sides. Most gorges have fast rivers flowing through them. Large gorges are sometimes called **canyons**.
The river flowed through the narrow gorge.

gradient *noun*
A gradient is a measure of **slope**. High up a hill or mountain, the gradient usually becomes steeper.
The mountain became more difficult to climb as the gradient increased.

granite *noun*
Granite is a kind of **igneous** rock or **stone**. Granite is hard, with a coarse grain and a pink or grey colour. Granite is a mixture of **feldspar**, **quartz** and **mica**.
The building was made entirely of granite.

graphite *noun*
Graphite is a **mineral**. It is a soft, dark grey form of pure **carbon**. Graphite is found in **metamorphic** rocks. It can be used to conduct heat. Graphite is slippery and can also be used as a lubricant.
The leads of pencils are made from graphite mixed with clay.

grassland *noun*
A grassland is a region where grass is the main kind of plant. Large grasslands are found in East Africa and in parts of central Asia. Grasslands occur where there is not enough **rainfall** for trees to grow well.
The grassland was ploughed up to grow crops.

gravel *noun*
Gravel is small pieces of rock, which range in size from 2 millimetres to 4 millimetres. Gravel pieces come between **sand** and **pebbles** in size.
Some kinds of desert are made up of gravel and small stones.

gravity *noun*
Gravity is a force which pulls objects towards the centre of the **Earth**. Gravity is also the force which gives the **planets** a regular movement around the Sun.
Gravity made the object fall to the floor when it was dropped.
gravitate *verb*

greenhouse effect *noun*
The greenhouse effect is a theory which describes the gradual warming of the **atmosphere** of the **Earth**. The greenhouse effect is thought to be caused by the build-up of **carbon dioxide** and **methane** in the atmosphere. These gases prevent heat escaping from the Earth's surface and the lower parts of the atmosphere.
Some scientists think that the greenhouse effect will cause average temperatures to rise by between 1 and 5 degrees Celsius by the year 2050.

Greenwich meridian *noun*
The Greenwich meridian is an imaginary line around the Earth's surface. It joins the **North Pole** and **South Pole** and crosses the **Equator** at a right angle. **Meridians** are a measure of **longitude**. The Greenwich meridian is 0 degrees longitude. All the other meridians are measured in **degrees** from the Greenwich meridian. The meridian takes its name from Greenwich in the British Isles, through which it passes.
We saw the sign marking the position of the Greenwich meridian.

grid *noun*
A grid is a system of two sets of lines that cross each other. The lines that make up the grid around the **Earth** are called lines of **longitude** and lines of **latitude**. A numbered grid is used on **maps**. On the map, grid numbers show the position of a place.
We reached the lake we were looking for by following the grid on the map.

Earth
line of longitude
line of latitude

grotto *noun*
A grotto is a kind of **cave**. Grottos are common in **limestone** areas where water has worn away the rock.
The river flowed into a large, dark grotto.

ground *noun*
Ground is a word used to describe the surface of the **land**. In rocky areas, the ground is very hard. Sometimes the ground can be soft and soggy, as in **marshes**, **bogs** and **fens**.
It was easy to build the house because the ground was firm and level.

geological time *noun*
Geological time is a description of the way
geologists divide up the Earth's known history.
The largest divisions are the four **eons**.
The most recent eon is divided into three
eras. The eras are divided in turn into
periods. The three most recent periods are
split into seven **epochs**.
Eons are part of geological time.

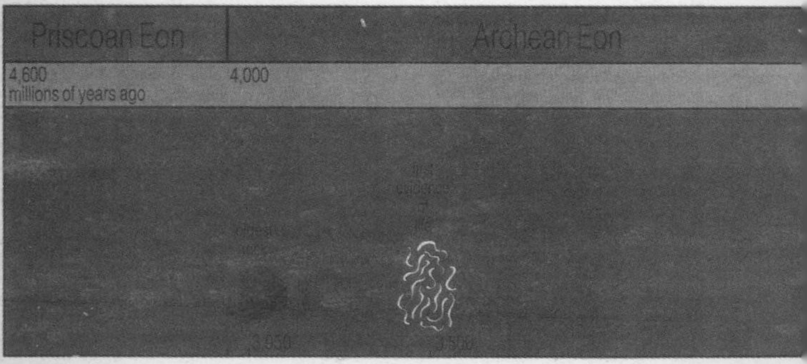

Priscoan Eon	Archean Eon
4,600 millions of years ago	4,000

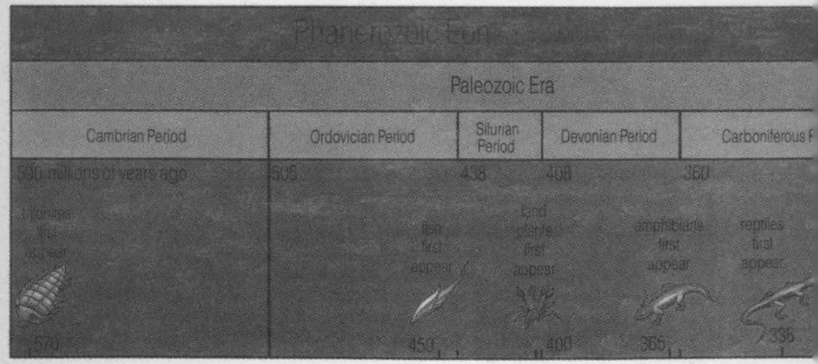

Phanerozoic Eon				
Paleozoic Era				
Cambrian Period	Ordovician Period	Silurian Period	Devonian Period	Carboniferous P
500 millions of years ago	505	438	408	360
trilobites first appear		fish first appear	land plants first appear	amphibians first appear	reptiles first appear
570	450	400	365	335

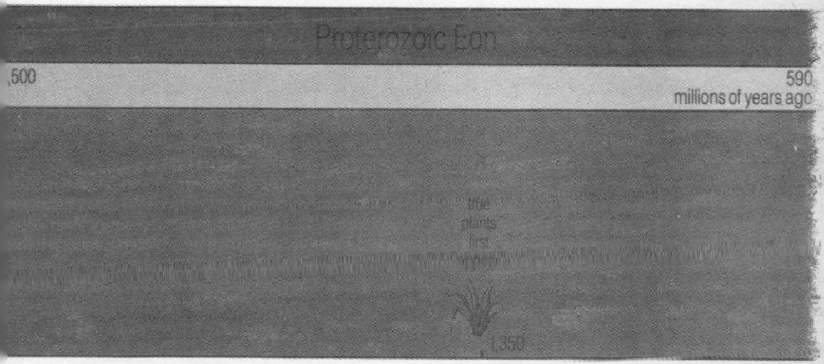

Proterozoic Eon

,500   590
millions of years ago

true
plants
first
appear

1,350

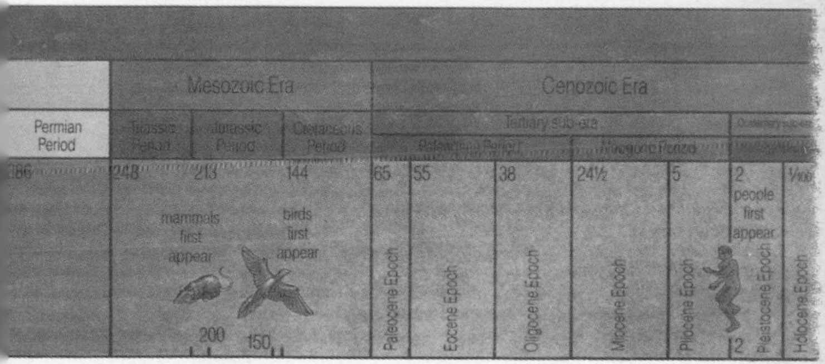

	Mesozoic Era			Cenozoic Era						
Permian Period	Triassic Period	Jurassic Period	Cretaceous Period	Tertiary sub-era					Quaternary sub-era	
				Paleogene Period			Neogene Period			
286	248	213	144	65	55	38	24½	5	2 people first appear	1/100
	mammals first appear	birds first appear		Paleocene Epoch	Eocene Epoch	Oligocene Epoch	Miocene Epoch	Pliocene Epoch	Pleistocene Epoch	Holocene Epoch
		200 150							2	

65

cier *noun*

acier is a river of **ice**, **rocks** and **soil**. It is
ned from densely packed **snow**, called
é, which never melts. Névé is pressed
n so hard that it turns to ice. The pressure
ntually forces the ice to move downhill.
st glaciers move only a few centimetres a
. Some steep glaciers make creaking
noises. Glaciers are found in high mountains
and also in Antarctica.
*We had to walk very carefully when crossing
the slippery glacier.*

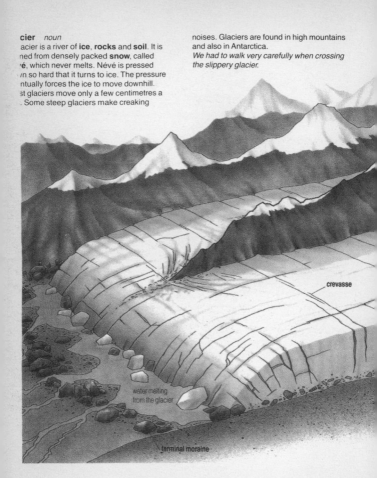

crevasse

water melting
from the glacier

terminal moraine

66

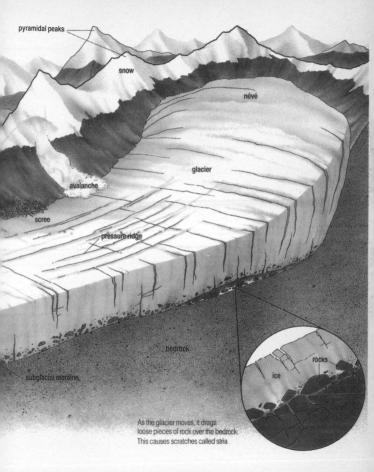

As the glacier moves, it drags
loose pieces of rock over the bedrock.
This causes scratches called stria.

67

ground frost   *noun*

Ground frost describes a **frost** which only freezes the surface of the **ground**. A ground frost is a light frost which usually does little damage to growing plants.

The weather forecast said that there would be a ground frost in the night.

ground water   *noun*

Ground water is water which soaks into **porous** rocks in the ground. **Springs** develop where there are rocks full of ground water at the surface of the Earth.

A deep well was sunk to pump up the ground water in the porous rocks.

gulf   *noun*

A gulf is a large area of sea which is almost enclosed by land. A famous gulf is the Persian Gulf, which lies between Iran and Saudi Arabia in the Middle East.

The ships sailed into the more sheltered waters of the gulf.

gully   *noun*

A gully is a narrow **channel** in rock or in the soil. Gullies are usually formed by **erosion**. Water may make a gully by wearing away soft earth or rock.

The stream had worn away a gully in the mud of the salt-marsh.

gypsum   *noun*

Gypsum is a **mineral**. Gypsum is found naturally either as **crystals** or as a fine-grained substance called **alabaster**. It is made of calcium sulphate.

Plaster of Paris is made from gypsum.

gyre   *noun*

A gyre is the circular movement of water. In some parts of the sea, the **currents** move in a gyre.

The ocean currents moved slowly round in the gyre.

H

hail *noun*
Hail is frozen raindrops. The **ice** pieces in hail are called hailstones. Hailstones may be as large as 5 centimetres in diameter.
The entire crop was flattened by the hail.

hamada *noun*
A hamada is a kind of **desert** where the surface of the ground is bare rock. Wind has swept away any loose material, and polished the surface of the rock.
There are areas of hamada in the Sahara in North Africa.

hanging valley *noun*
A hanging valley is a geological **feature**. A hanging valley meets a larger **valley** at a point high up on the side of the larger valley. Hanging valleys were formed by the action of **glaciers**.
The hanging valley lay at the top of a steep slope.

hard water *noun*
Hard water is water which contains large amounts of dissolved **calcium** and **magnesium** salts. Hard water is often found in **limestone** areas.
The hard water left a layer of calcium in the water pipes.

haze *noun*
Haze describes a very thin **mist**. It also describes the effect of warm **air** rising through cooler air. This is called a heat haze.
It was difficult to see clearly because of the haze.

headland *noun*
A headland is a narrow piece of land jutting out into the **sea**. Headlands often end in **cliffs** which fall steeply to the sea. Many lighthouses are built on headlands.
The boat came into view as it rounded the headland.

heat *noun*
Heat is the **energy** we feel when the **temperature** of an object or substance increases. Heat is given out when **fuel** is burned. The Sun also gives out heat, which warms the surface of the Earth. Heat is measured in units called joules.
They had to shade themselves from the heat of the desert Sun.

heavy mineral *noun*
A heavy mineral is a mineral that has a large mass. When it is a powder it will sink in a liquid. **Zircon** and **iron** are heavy minerals.
The geologist separated the heavy minerals from the mixture.

hectare *noun*
A hectare is a metric unit of measurement. It measures area. One hectare is equal to 10,000 square metres.
The trees covered about 5 hectares.

helium *noun*
Helium is an **element**. It is a very light **gas**. Helium is an **inert** gas, so it does not react with other elements.
Helium is used to fill balloons and airships because it is lighter than air.

hematite *noun*
Hematite is a **mineral**. It is a kind of **iron** oxide and has a reddish colour. Hematite is found in **igneous** rocks and also in some types of **sandstone**.
Hematite is used as an ore in the production of iron.

hemisphere *noun*
Hemisphere describes one half of the **globe**. The northern and southern hemispheres are separated by the **Equator**.
There is more land in the northern hemisphere than in the southern hemisphere.

high pressure *noun*
High pressure is an area of the air where the **atmospheric pressure** is high. It is also known as an **anticyclone** and is the opposite of a **depression**. High pressure areas usually bring clear, dry weather.
The clouds disappeared as the high pressure arrived.

hill *noun*
A hill is a high area of the **landscape** with a definite **summit**. Hills rise up from the surrounding **lowland**. Some hills are single and others are found in **ranges**. Hills can vary in size from a few metres high to several hundred metres. A hill is not as high as a **mountain**.
The village lay at the bottom of the hill.

hoar frost *noun*
Hoar frost is a kind of frost which is produced when the air near the ground cools down very fast at night. Hoar frost coats the grass and trees with **crystals** of **ice**.
In the morning, the hoar frost sparkled in the garden.

hollow *noun*
A hollow is a shallow dip in the surface of the ground. Some hollows form when the ground below collapses. Other hollows are caused by the action of ice.
There was a lake at the bottom of the hollow.

Holocene *adjective*
Holocene describes the most recent **epoch** in **geological time**. It began about 10,000 years ago and continues today. The word Holocene means recent.
Mammoths died out just before the Holocene Epoch.

horizon *noun*
Horizon describes a horizontal **layer**, or **stratum**, either in the soil or in rocks. Horizon is also the point in the distance at which the land seems to meet the sky.
The fossils were all found at one particular horizon within the rocks.

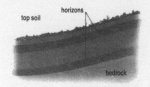

top soil
horizons
bedrock

hornblende *noun*
Hornblende is a **mineral**. It is dark green or brown. Hornblende is made of **sodium**, **calcium**, **magnesium**, **iron** and **aluminium**, combined with **silica**.
They found hornblende in the granite rocks.

hot-spot *noun*
A hot-spot is a region in the Earth's **mantle** where molten rocks, or **magma**, rise upwards through the **crust**. A **volcano** forms where a hot-spot reaches the surface of the Earth.
The geologist showed us a map of the Earth's hot-spots.

hot spring *noun*
A hot spring is a **spring** in which the water comes out at a high **temperature**. Hot springs are found where there is **volcanic** activity near the surface of the Earth.
Iceland and New Zealand are famous for their hot springs.

humid *adjective*
Humid describes the **atmosphere** when it contains a large amount of water **vapour**. Warm air holds more water vapour than cold air, so it can be more humid.
The air in a tropical rain forest is very humid.

humidity *noun*
Humidity is a measure of the level of water **vapour** in the **atmosphere**. When air is completely saturated with water vapour, it reaches its **dew point** and the water **condenses** as droplets.
We began to sweat because the humidity was so high.

humus *noun*
Humus is the **organic** material in soil. It is made up of the remains of plants and animals. It is a rich source of the **chemicals** needed by growing plants.
Fallen leaves decompose and turn into humus in the soil.

hurricane ▶ page 72

hydro- *prefix*
Hydro- is a prefix which means to do with water.
The hydro-electric power station made electricity from the flow of water.

hydrocarbon *noun*
A hydrocarbon is a **compound** made of **hydrogen** and **carbon**. Hydrocarbons are the most important chemicals found in **oil** and they are used to make **fuels**.
Methane gas is an example of a hydrocarbon.

hydro-electric power *noun*
Hydro-electric power is made by turning the **energy** of moving water into electricity. Water from a **reservoir** flows rapidly through a **dam**. This fast-flowing water spins a turbine which generates electricity.
Hydro-electric power is an important source of energy in mountainous areas with a high rainfall.

hydro-electric power station

hydrogen *noun*
Hydrogen is the lightest of all the **elements**. It is a **gas**. Hydrogen is usually found in **compounds**, especially in water and in **hydrocarbons** such as methane.
Water is made up of hydrogen combined with oxygen.

hydrography *noun*
Hydrography is the making of **maps** or **charts** of the waters of the world. It includes describing and surveying rivers, lakes, oceans and the coast.
She studied the science of hydrography in order to map the coastal waters.

hydrology *noun*
Hydrology is the study of **water** in the **environment**. It involves studying rivers and **oceans**, as well as water in the ground and in the air.
The hydrology of the area had to be studied to understand the flow of the river.

hurricane *noun*

A hurricane is the strongest kind of **wind**.
A hurricane blows in a circular pattern. There
is an area of calm air, called the eye, in the
centre of a hurricane. The winds of a
hurricane are accompanied by heavy **rain**
and **thunderstorms**. A hurricane measures
force 12 on the **Beaufort Scale**. In South-east
Asia a hurricane is called a **typhoon**.
The whole village was destroyed when the
hurricane passed through it.

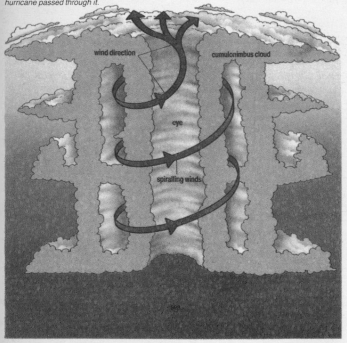

hydrolysis *noun*
Hydrolysis is the chemical **weathering** of rocks. Water combines with minerals in the rocks to make **salts** which cannot dissolve. Hydrolysis often takes place in **igneous** rocks which contain **silica**. Hydrolysis usually leads to **clay** being formed.
The rocks showed clear signs of hydrolysis.

hydrosphere *noun*
The hydrosphere describes all the natural **water** found on the **Earth**. The hydrosphere includes the oceans, rivers, lakes, underground water and the water **vapour** in the **atmosphere**.
Life on Earth depends on the hydrosphere because all living things need water.

hydroxide *noun*
A hydroxide is a chemical **compound** which contains **hydrogen** and **oxygen**. Water is the hydroxide of hydrogen. Another hydroxide is caustic soda, which is sodium hydroxide.
They cleaned the stains with sodium hydroxide.

hygrometer *noun*
A hygrometer is an instrument used for measuring the **humidity** of the **atmosphere**. One kind of hygrometer has two **thermometers**, one dry and one wet. The difference in **temperature** between the two gives a measure of humidity.
While it was raining, the hygrometer reading was 1.

hygroscope *noun*
A hygroscope records changes in the **humidity** of the **atmosphere**. A strip of seaweed can be used as a simple hygroscope. When the atmosphere is **humid**, the seaweed feels soft and bends easily. When the atmosphere is dry, the seaweed is hard and dry.
While it was raining, the hygroscope reading remained steady.

ice *noun*
Ice is frozen **water**. Pure water freezes at 0 **degrees** Celsius. Salt water freezes at a lower temperature, so the sea freezes only when it is very cold. When water becomes ice, it swells and takes up more space. Ice is lighter than water, so it floats on the surface of water.
The water turned to ice inside the crack in the rock and made the crack bigger.

ice floating on the water

Ice Age *noun*
An Ice Age is a period when the **climate** is very cold. It can last for many centuries. During an Ice Age, **ice-sheets** and **glaciers** cover large areas of the Earth. The most recent Ice Age was about 15,000 years ago.
During the last Ice Age, most of northern Europe was covered by ice.

iceberg *noun*
An iceberg is a large piece of **ice** floating in the sea. Icebergs break off from **ice-sheets** or from **glaciers** and drift on ocean **currents**. Only about one ninth of an iceberg can be seen above the water.
The liner called the Titanic hit an iceberg during its first ocean crossing and sank.

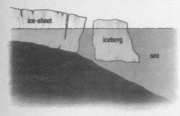

ice-cap *noun*
An ice-cap is a covering of **ice** on an area of land. Some mountains have permanent ice-caps. An ice-cap is larger than a **glacier**, but smaller and thinner than an **ice-sheet**. The **South Pole** lies on the Antarctic ice-cap.
Some of the Earth's oldest rocks are found at the edge of the Greenland ice-cap.

ice-field *noun*
An ice-field is an area of **ice** which is floating in the **sea**. It usually measures more than 10 kilometres across.
The explorers crossed many ice-fields on their way to the North Pole.

ice-floe *noun*
An ice-floe is a flat piece of **ice**, adrift in the sea. Ice-floes often break away from the edges of **ice-fields**. Ice-floes are common in the cold seas of the **Arctic** and **Antarctica**. They vary in size from a few metres to several hundred metres wide.
The sea around the ice-field was dotted with ice-floes.

ice-sheet *noun*
An ice-sheet is a large, thick layer of **ice** covering an area of land. There are many ice-sheets in Greenland and in **Antarctica**. Ice-sheets are bigger and thicker than **ice-caps**.
The flat ice-sheet stretched away as far as they could see.

icicle *noun*
An icicle is a hanging spike of clear **ice**. It forms from dripping water. As the water trickles down the icicle, it freezes. This gradually makes the icicle thicker and longer. Icicles often hang from the roofs of houses in very cold weather.
In the morning, there was an icicle on the tap.

igneous *adjective*
Igneous describes a kind of **rock** or **stone**. The other kinds are **sedimentary** and **metamorphic** rocks. Igneous rocks are formed from molten material inside the Earth. Some igneous rocks form underground. Others form from the **lava** thrown out by an erupting **volcano**.
The slopes of the volcano were made of igneous rocks.

illite *noun*
Illite is a common **clay** mineral. It is found in some soils and on the **sea-bed**. The name comes from Illinois in the United States of America, where it is very common. Some plants cannot grow well on soil which contains illite as the illite absorbs the **potassium** and ammonium that the plants need.
The geologist found that the soil contained large amounts of illite.

impermeable *adjective*
Impermeable describes something through which **water** cannot pass. The opposite of impermeable is **permeable**.
The water collected in the hollow above a layer of impermeable clay.

impervious *adjective*
Impervious describes materials through which water cannot pass. Rocks which do not have gaps or cracks may be impervious. The opposite of impervious is **pervious**.
The stone building was impervious to water.

impurity *noun*
An impurity is a small amount of another substance found in a pure substance. Sometimes, an impurity can change the pure substance. Pure **corundum** is a colourless **crystal**. But crystals of corundum that contain **chromium** are red **rubies**.
He filtered out the impurity to obtain pure water.

inert *adjective*
Inert describes **gases** which do not react easily with other **chemicals**. Inert gases include **helium**, **neon**, **argon**, **krypton** and **radon**.
The fluorescent light bulb contained inert gases.

infertile *adjective*
Infertile describes something that cannot support growth. Plants cannot grow in infertile **soil**. Infertile also describes an animal or plant which cannot produce young or seeds.
The crops did not grow because the ground was infertile.

inland *adjective*
Inland is a word that describes land that is away from the sea, in the middle of a country or region.
The inland road took them away from the sea and towards the mountains.

inlet *noun*
An inlet is a short, narrow opening which runs **inland** from a large stretch of water. **Lakes** and **coasts** often have many inlets.
The canoe moved slowly between the banks of the narrow inlet.

inner core *noun*
The inner core is the central part of the **Earth**. It lies about 4,500 kilometres deep and is surrounded by the **outer core**. The inner core is solid and is mainly made of **iron** and **nickel**. The inner core of the Earth is a **magnet**. Scientists think the temperature is about 2,700 degrees Celsius.
The diagram showed the inner core as a ball of molten metal at the centre of the Earth.

inorganic *adjective*
Inorganic is the word used to describe substances which do not contain any of the **organic** chemicals that make up living things. The rocks of the Earth's **crust** are inorganic. The opposite of inorganic is organic.
There were layers of coal among the inorganic rocks.

intensity *noun*
Intensity is the word used to describe the force of a natural event, such as an **earthquake**. The intensity of an earthquake is measured on the **Richter Scale**. Intensity is also used to describe **rainfall**. Rainfall can be heavy, moderate or light in intensity.
The intensity of the earthquake was so great that the city was completely destroyed.

inter- *prefix*
Inter- is a prefix meaning between or among.
An international deal lets scientists from many countries work in Antarctica.

interglacial period   *noun*
An interglacial period is the time between two periods of **glaciation**. During an interglacial period, the **temperature** on the Earth is higher than during glaciation, **glaciers** melt and the **sea-level** may rise.
The ice-sheets melted in the warmer temperatures of the interglacial period.

International Date Line   *noun*
The International Date Line is an imaginary line drawn through the Pacific Ocean. It runs mostly along the 180 degrees **meridian**. It is where each new calendar day begins. When it is Monday to the west of the line, it will be Sunday to the east of the line.
This will be an eight-day week because we will travel to the east across the International Date Line and have two Sundays.

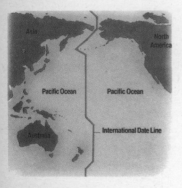

intertidal zone   *noun*
The intertidal zone is an area of the **sea-shore**. It is covered by water at high **tide** and is dry at low tide. It is part of the **littoral zone**. Some animals and plants are found only in the intertidal zone.
In many parts of the world, the sea covers the intertidal zone twice each day.

intrusion   *noun*
An intrusion is a piece of **igneous** rock found inside another rock. An intrusion squeezes into other rocks when it is **molten**. **Gems** and **minerals** can be found in intrusions.
The geologist showed us the intrusion in the rock face.

inversion   *noun*
An inversion describes a change which is exactly the opposite to what is normally experienced. A **temperature** inversion can happen when the air becomes warmer with **altitude**, rather than colder. It can also happen in some lakes when the deep water is warmer than the water at the surface.
The temperature inversion resulted in frost covering the bottom of the valley.

iodine   *noun*
Iodine is an **element**. It is composed of greyish-black **crystals**. All living things need iodine to grow. Some iodine **compounds** can be used to prevent infection.
Her mother put a special kind of iodine on her cut knee to disinfect it.

ionosphere   *noun*
The ionosphere is part of the Earth's **atmosphere**. The ionosphere lies above the **stratopause**, starting about 80 kilometres above the surface of the Earth.
Many magnetic storms take place in the ionosphere.

iron   *noun*
Iron is an **element**. It is a dark grey **metal**. Iron reacts with damp air to form rust, which is a reddish-brown colour. Iron is a very common element in the Earth's **crust**.
The iron nail became rusty in the moist air.

iron ore   *noun*
Iron ore is a **mineral** which contains **iron**. There are several different kinds of iron ore. The main ones are called **hematite**, **magnetite**, **limonite** and **pyrite**.
The factory made iron from iron ore.

irrigation *noun*

Irrigation is the method of taking **water** to dry land where there is not enough rainfall for crops to grow. The water is carried in **canals** and ditches from a river or other source of water and spread by sprinklers or pipes.
Crops can be grown in desert areas where irrigation provides water.

irrigate *verb*

island *noun*

An island is an area of **land** entirely surrounded by **water**. An island can be only a few metres across or many thousands of kilometres wide. The largest island on Earth is the **continent** of Australia.
We sailed right around the island in a day.

iso- *prefix*

Iso- is a prefix meaning equal.
The isotherm lines on our map showed us which places had equal temperature.

isobar *noun*

An isobar is a line drawn on a weather **map** to join points of equal **pressure**. If the isobars on a weather map are close together, the winds are strong.
We knew it would be calm, because the isobars were far apart.

isobath *noun*

An isobath is a line drawn on a **chart** of the sea or a lake. An isobath joins points on the **sea-bed** or on the bottom of a lake which are at the same depth from the surface.
The isobath showed where the water was shallow, so we steered the boat away.

isotherm *noun*

An isotherm is a line on a weather **map** which joins places where the **temperature** is the same.
The isotherm showed that the temperature that day was the same in Denver as it was in New York.

isthmus *noun*

An isthmus is a long, narrow strip of land which joins together two large **land masses**. There is sea on either side of an isthmus.
The Isthmus of Panama joins North America and South America and lies between the Atlantic and Pacific oceans.

J   K

jade   *noun*
Jade is a hard, semi-precious stone which is used as a **gem**. It can be many colours, including green, white, brown or orange. Jade is made up of jadeite or **nephrite**. Nephrite is the more common of the two **minerals** and is mostly found in New Zealand.
Jade can be carved into delicate shapes because it is so tough.

jet   *noun*
Jet is a hard form of **coal**. When it is cut and polished, it is very shiny and looks like black glass. It is used to make jewellery and ornaments.
The earrings were made from bright, black stones of jet.

jet stream   *noun*
The jet stream is a narrow band of fast-moving **winds** which is found at high **altitudes**. There are several jet streams and they change position and speed at different times of the year.
The plane travelled in the jet stream and arrived ahead of schedule.

Jurassic   *adjective*
Jurassic describes a **period** in **geological time**. The Jurassic Period lasted from about 213 million years ago to about 144 million years ago. The biggest **dinosaurs** lived in the Jurassic Period.
Some of today's species of fern were also growing during the Jurassic Period.

kaolin   ▶ **China clay**

Karroo   *noun*
The Karroo is an area of southern Africa where the **climate** is very dry. The plants of the Karroo have adapted to living in dry conditions.
Farmers must use irrigation to grow crops in the Karroo.

karst   *noun*
Karst is the name for a special kind of **landscape**. It is found in areas where there are **limestone** rocks near the surface. Karst regions have many underground streams and rivers, where the water has worn passages through the limestone.
Karst areas are well known for their deep caves.

key   *noun*
A key, or cay, is a small, flat **island**. It is made of **sand** that has built up in shallow water. The surface of the island lies only just above the water at high **tide**. Keys are found in **coral reefs** and in Florida in the United States of America.
The sailors could see the keys on the horizon.

L

khamsin   *noun*
The khamsin is a **wind**. It is very hot, dry and dusty and blows from the south, across the Sahara in north Africa. The khamsin usually blows from April to June.
We had to drink plenty of water when the khamsin blew.

kieselguhr   *noun*
Kieselguhr is a rock. It is soft and fine-grained. It is made up of the shells of tiny plants which lived in water. Kieselguhr has many uses in industry.
The impurities in the water were removed as it filtered through the bed of kieselguhr.

knoll   *noun*
A knoll is a small, rounded **hill**.
The children rolled the ball down the slope of the grassy knoll.

krypton   *noun*
Krypton is an **element**. It is a **gas** which is found in small amounts in the **atmosphere**. Krypton forms very few **compounds** with other elements. It is called an **inert** gas.
The fluorescent lamp was filled with a mixture of gases, including krypton.

labradorite   *noun*
Labradorite is a **mineral**. It is a greyish-white kind of **feldspar**. In the light, labradorite may show blue, green and red colours, especially where it is cut. It was first found at Labrador in Canada.
The building was decorated with pretty labradorite stones.

lagoon   *noun*
A lagoon is a shallow pool of salt water near the **coast**. A lagoon is usually cut off from the sea by a ridge of sand or **shingle**. In an **atoll** the central lagoon is surrounded by a **coral reef**.
We swam safely in the lagoon because the water was so shallow.

lake   *noun*
A lake is a large piece of water which is completely surrounded by land. Most lakes contain fresh water, but there are also some salt-water lakes. Some lakes have rivers flowing through them.
The rowing boats were out on the lake throughout the summer.

land   *noun*
Land is the solid part of the surface of the **Earth**. The Earth's surface is covered by land, sea and fresh water.
The surveyor mapped the land.

land mass   *noun*
A land mass is a large piece of **land**.
A **continent** is a land mass.
The land mass around the South Pole is called Antarctica.

landscape   *noun*
Landscape is a word which describes an area
of country. Landscape includes the natural
scenery, buildings and roads.
The landscape was dotted with trees.

landslide   *noun*
A landslide is a fall of rocks and earth down a
steep **slope**. A landslide can happen after
heavy rain has loosened the surface of the
soil. **Earthquakes** and **mining** can also
cause landslides.
*The whole village was buried under the
landslide.*

lapilli   *noun*
Lapilli are small pieces of volcanic material.
Lapilli are only a few millimetres across. They
are thrown out of a **volcano** when it **erupts**.
*The lapilli fell to the ground some distance
from the volcano.*

lapis lazuli   *noun*
Lapis lazuli is a deep blue, semi-precious
stone. It is made mostly of the blue **mineral**
lazurite and also contains the mineral **calcite**.
*A deep blue paint can be made from
powdered lapis lazuli.*

large-scale   *adjective*
Large-scale is a term used when something
is shown in great detail. A large-scale **map**
covers all the features of a small area.
A large-scale diagram is drawn large enough
to show a very detailed view of the subject.
*We used the large-scale map to follow the
footpath.*

laterite   *noun*
Laterite is a **soil**. Laterite is red and sandy
and contains **iron** and **aluminium** oxides. It is
formed by the **weathering** of certain kinds of
rock, mostly **volcanic** rock, in the **tropics**.
The red road was made from crushed laterite.

latitude   *noun*
Latitude is an imaginary line around the Earth,
parallel to the **Equator**. It is used to measure
distance from the Equator. There are
90 **degrees** of latitude on each side of the
Equator. Places of equal distance from the
Equator lie on the same **parallel** of latitude.
On **maps**, latitude measures the vertical
position of a point. The horizontal distance is
measured by **longitude**.
*The Equator is 0 degrees latitude and the
poles are 90 degrees latitude.*

Laurasia   *noun*
Laurasia is the name of a large **continent**.
Some scientists think that it formed when
the **super-continent** of Pangaea split about
215 million years ago, during the **Mesozoic**
Era. Laurasia may have gradually split
further, to create North America, Greenland,
Europe and Asia.
*Some scientists think there was a large
continent in the northern hemisphere called
Laurasia.*

lava   *noun*
Lava is the **molten** rock which comes out of a
volcano when it **erupts**, or from cracks in the
Earth. Lava cools to form **igneous** rock.
*We could see the lava flowing down the
slopes of the volcano.*

red-hot lava flow

layer *noun*
Layer is a thickness of rock. Each **stratum** in **sedimentary** rock consists of a number of layers.
The geologists found many fossils in one particular layer of the rock.

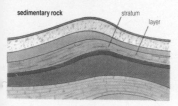
sedimentary rock — stratum — layer

leach *verb*
Leach describes the effects of water as it moves down into the soil. The water removes **salts** from the upper layers of the soil and carries them further down into the ground. When a soil is leached, the top layers become less **fertile**. Leaching can cause **acid soil**. But some farmers leach ground to wash away harmful salts.
The heavy rains leached the soil.

lead *noun*
Lead is an **element**. It is a very heavy, dark grey **metal**. There are several lead **ores**. The most common is **galena**. Lead can be used as a building material, in **alloys** with other metals and in many other ways.
They found lead pellets in the dead bird.

levee *noun*
A levee is a raised **bank** beside a **river**. The levee is higher than the land beyond the river. Levees form when rivers **flood** and the **sediment** from the water is deposited on the edge of the river **channel**. Levees can be built along the sides of a river to stop it flooding the land.
By walking along the levee, they could see over the river and the fields.

level *noun*
A level is an instrument for measuring height. It is used by map-makers and surveyors. A level measures how high one point is above another point.
The surveyor used his level to find the height of the hill.

lightning *noun*
Lightning is an electric spark from a **cloud** in a **thunderstorm**. Lightning can be seen as flashes, as balls, or as sheets of light. It is followed by **thunder**.
The lightning lit up the night sky.

forked lightning

lignite *noun*
Lignite, or brown coal, is a kind of **fossil fuel**. It burns with a very smoky flame. Lignite is a form of **coal**. It contains about 65 per cent **carbon**. Lignite has more carbon in it than **peat**, but less than **anthracite**.
The power station burned lignite to make electricity.

lime *noun*
Lime is a solid, white **compound**. It is also the name used for **salts** of **calcium**. The two forms of lime are quicklime and slaked lime. Quicklime is an **oxide** of calcium and is used as a **fertilizer**. When water is added, quicklime becomes calcium hydroxide. This is slaked lime which is used in cements.
The farmer spread a layer of lime on the field.

limestone *noun*
Limestone is a kind of **sedimentary** rock. It is often used as a building **stone** because it is easy to cut. Limestone is used to make **lime**. Many plants grow well on limestone soils.
The limestone cliffs shone white in the Sun.

limonite *noun*
Limonite is a **mineral**. It is a yellow-brown kind of **iron ore**. Very pure iron can be extracted from limonite.
They found lumps of limonite in the soil.

lithium *noun*
Lithium is an **element**. It is a soft, silvery **metal**. Pure lithium cannot be found because it joins with other elements so easily. Lithium is used in batteries, for **alloys** and in medicine.
The lithium batteries were expensive.

lithosphere *noun*
The lithosphere is the Earth's **crust** and the top of the **mantle**. It includes the **tectonic plates**. The lithosphere is one part of the outer area of the Earth. The other parts are the **atmosphere** and the **hydrosphere**.
The Earth's rocks and minerals form part of the lithosphere.

littoral zone *noun*
The littoral zone is the area of water and land at the edge of the **sea-shore** and of lakes. The littoral zone includes the **intertidal** zone and slightly deeper water.
They picked up the shells in the littoral zone.

loam *noun*
Loam is a kind of **soil**. It is a mixture of **sand**, **silt** and small amounts of **clay**. Loams are very **fertile** soils.
The farmer grew a good crop of carrots in the deep loam.

lode *noun*
A lode is a **vein** of **minerals** which runs through rock. The lode may be mined, if the mineral is valuable.
The mining engineers found gold deposits in the lode.

lodestone *noun*
Lodestone is a kind of **iron ore** which works as a **magnet**. It is made of **magnetite**. Pieces of lodestone were used as an early form of **compass**. Some of the most powerful lodestones are found in Russia and South Africa.
The explorers used a lodestone to work out the direction they needed to take.

loess *noun*
Loess is a kind of **soil**. It is yellow-coloured, light and rich in **lime**. Loess soils are very **fertile**. Loess can be used to make bricks. Large areas of loess are found in central Europe, the United States of America and in China.
The farmer planted his crops in the deep loess.

longitude *noun*
Longitude is an imaginary line around the Earth. It starts at the **North Pole** and finishes at the **South Pole**. Longitude is a measurement used for distance eastward or westward. All longitudes are measured in **degrees** from the **Greenwich meridian**, which is 0 degrees longitude. On **maps**, longitude measures the horizontal position of a point. The vertical position is measured by **latitude**.
There are 360 degrees of longitude around the Earth.

low pressure *noun*
Low pressure is an area of the **atmosphere** where **atmospheric pressure** is low. During a period of low pressure, or **depression**, the weather is often wet.
The low pressure made the weather windy and cold.

lowlands *noun*
Lowlands is the word used for land which is flat or gently rolling, and which is lower than the land around it. Higher ground with **mountains** is called highlands.
The farmer brought the sheep down to the lowlands for the winter.

lustre *noun*
Lustre is the shine on the surface of a **mineral**. Different kinds of stones and minerals have different lustres.
The lustre of the ore made it very beautiful.
lustrous *adjective*

M

magma *noun*
Magma is **molten** rock which contains **gases**. Magma is formed in the Earth's **mantle**. It sometimes comes to the surface as **lava** when **volcanoes** erupt, or through cracks in the Earth. When magma cools, it forms **igneous** rocks and **stones**.
After the eruption, the magma cooled on the sides of the volcano.

magnesium *noun*
Magnesium is an **element**. It is a silvery-grey **metal**. Magnesium is found in many **minerals** and also in sea water. It burns with a very bright flame.
They sent up magnesium flares from the boat to show the rescuers their position.

magnet *noun*
A magnet is an object, usually made of **metal**, which attracts other metal objects. Magnets have two **magnetic poles**. The **core** of the **Earth** acts as a giant magnet.
The needle on a compass is a magnet.
magnetic *adjective*

magnetic field *noun*
A magnetic field is the area affected by a **magnet**. The **Earth** is surrounded by a magnetic field.
The compass worked in the magnetic field.

magnetic north *noun*
Magnetic north is the position of the **magnetic pole** at the northern point of the **Earth**. It is in Canada, near the geographic **North Pole**.
The explorer walked towards magnetic north.

magnetic pole *noun*

A magnetic pole is an area of strong magnetic force at the end of a **magnet**. The **Earth** is a magnet, and has a magnetic pole at either end of its magnetic field. The **magnetic north** pole and the **magnetic south** pole are some distance away from the geographical **North Pole** and **South Pole**.

The exact positions of the magnetic poles change slowly.

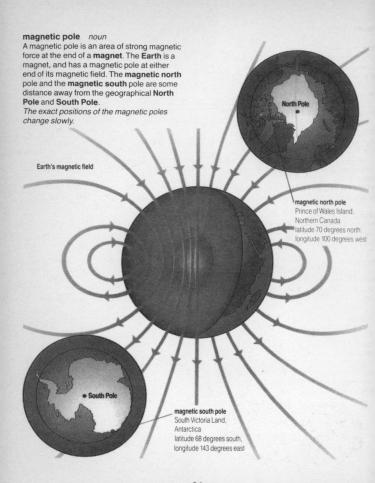

Earth's magnetic field

North Pole

magnetic north pole
Prince of Wales Island,
Northern Canada
latitude 70 degrees north,
longitude 100 degrees west

South Pole

magnetic south pole
South Victoria Land,
Antarctica
latitude 68 degrees south,
longitude 143 degrees east

84

magnetic pole ▶ page 84

magnetic south *noun*
Magnetic south is the position of the
magnetic pole at the southern point of the
Earth. The magnetic south is in the **continent**
of **Antarctica**, near the geographic
South Pole.
*The magnetic needle swung towards
magnetic south.*

magnetic storm *noun*
A magnetic storm is a disturbance in the
Earth's **magnetic field**. It is caused by
changes in the activity of the Sun. Magnetic
storms can interfere with radio waves and
satellites.
*Radio reception was poor because there was
a magnetic storm.*

magnetite *noun*
Magnetite, or **lodestone**, is a kind of black
iron ore. It contains **crystals** of iron **oxide**.
Magnetite is strongly **magnetic**.
*The rock contained sparkling pieces of
magnetite.*

magnitude *noun*
Magnitude describes the force of an
earthquake. The magnitude of an earthquake
is measured on the **Richter Scale**.
*Although the earthquake had a low
magnitude, it caused a lot of damage.*

malachite *noun*
Malachite is a **mineral**. It is bright green and
made of copper **carbonate**. Copper can be
extracted from malachite. Malachite is also
used as a semi-precious stone.
She wore a brooch of malachite.

manganese *noun*
Manganese is an **element**. It is a hard **metal**
which is found as manganese **oxide** in some
rocks. Manganese also occurs in **clay** and in
the **mud** on the ocean floor. All plants and
animals need a small amount of manganese
to grow properly.
*The tomato crop was poor because there was
not enough manganese in the soil.*

mantle *noun*
The mantle is the part of the **Earth** that lies
between the **crust** and the **core**. The mantle
is mostly solid **rock**, but some of the rocks are
molten. The movements of molten rock in the
mantle cause **continental drift** and **sea-floor
spreading**.
*Earth scientists are still discovering more
about the Earth's mantle.*

map ▶ page 86

marble *noun*
Marble is **limestone** changed to
metamorphic rock. It is very hard, and can be
cut and polished. Marble is used as a building
stone. Pure marble is white, but if it contains
impurities, it has mottled or veined patterns.
*The statue in the centre of the room was
made of marble.*

marine *adjective*
Marine is a word which describes anything to
do with the sea. Marine **abrasion** occurs
along **coasts** when the waves push **sand** and
shingle backwards and forwards.
*Marine biologists study all the things that live
in the sea.*

maritime *adjective*
Maritime describes something which is
near the sea or which is affected by the sea.
A maritime climate is **temperate**, and has
mild weather all year. The temperatures do
not change much from **winter** to **summer**,
and there is no dry season.
*The maritime provinces of Canada are those
which are next to the Atlantic Ocean.*

map *noun*

A map is a **scale** drawing of a country or a region For example, one centimetre of distance on the map may stand for one kilometre of distance on the surface of the Earth. Maps show features of the landscape, such as hills, roads and rivers in diagrammatic form

The relief map and the contour map show different views of the same place.

relief map

source

mountains

valley

tributary

meander

hills

lake

watershed

river

plateau

bight

river

coral islands and reefs

estuary

volcano

bay

peninsula

oasis

gulf

inlet

desert

cape or headland

marsh

lagoon

archipelago

delta

channel

islands

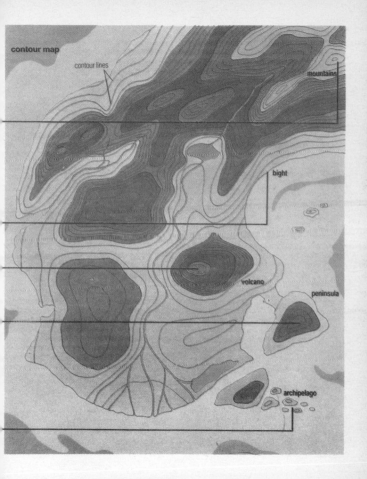

contour map

contour lines

mountains

bight

volcano

peninsula

archipelago

marsh *noun*

A marsh is an area of low, wet ground. In a marsh, the **drainage** is poor and the water often floods over the surface. Marshes can form at **estuaries** when the land becomes flooded with salt water.
We could see over the flat marsh to the sea.

massif *noun*

A massif is a large **mountain** or group of mountains. A massif stands out clearly from the surrounding **lowlands**.
The massif towered over the landscape and could be seen from far away.

matter *noun*

Matter is anything which has mass and takes up space. The three kinds of matter are solids, liquids and **gases**. Matter and **energy** together make up the whole universe.
Many scientists think that the Earth is made from matter which came from the Sun.

meander *noun*

A meander is a snake-like bend in a **river**. Lowland rivers often have many meanders along their length. Sometimes, a meander is cut off from the rest of the river and becomes an **ox-bow lake**.
The river flowed in a series of meanders.

Mercalli Scale ► page 89

Mercator projection *noun*

The Mercator projection is a way of drawing a **map** of the **Earth**. It is a cylindrical **projection**. On the Mercator projection, all the lines of **latitude** and **longitude** are drawn parallel to each other. On this projection, the countries near the **poles** seem larger than they really are.
Maps drawn with a Mercator projection are often used for navigation.

mercury *noun*

Mercury is an **element**. It is a silvery **metal**. Mercury is the only metal which is liquid at room **temperature**. Mercury is used in **thermometers** and in **alloys**.
When the Sun came out, the temperature rose and the mercury moved quickly up the thermometer.

meridian *noun*

A meridian is an imaginary line around the **Earth**. The meridians run from the **North Pole** to the **South Pole** and cross the **Equator** at a right angle. Meridians are measurements of **longitude**. They are numbered from 0 to 180 degrees to the east and to the west of the **Greenwich meridian**. The Greenwich meridian is 0 degrees longitude.
The meridian at 60 degrees west passes through the centre of South America.

Earth

Equator

lines of meridian

ercalli Scale *noun*

e Mercalli Scale is a scale used for
easuring the amount of damage caused
an **earthquake**. It has 12 grades. The
ength of an earthquake is now usually
easured on the **Richter Scale**.
e violent earthquake measured 10 on the
ercalli Scale.

can be recorded
ut not felt by people

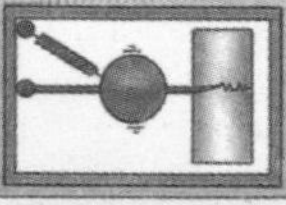

2
elt by a few people

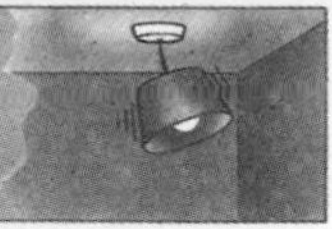

3
elt indoors, stationary
cars may rock

4
ears rock, windows
and dishes rattle,
pictures swing

5
sleepers roused,
plaster falls, windows
and dishes break

6
people frightened,
furniture moves,
chimneys damaged,
small bells ring

7
people run from buildings,
badly-built structures
damaged, large bells ring,
waves formed on ponds

8
general alarm,
more buildings damaged,
furniture overturned

9
panic, most buildings
damaged, some destroyed,
underground pipes break

10
panic, most buildings
and some bridges
destroyed, rails
slightly bent, landslides

11
panic, few buildings
survive, rails badly bent,
underground pipes all
damaged

12
panic, total destruction

mesa *noun*
A mesa is an isolated **hill** with a flat top, like a table. A mesa has a **cliff** or steep slope at the edges. Mesas are mostly found in dry **climates**.
There were caves at the base of the mesa.

Mesozoic *adjective*
Mesozoic describes one of the three major **eras** in **geological time**. The Mesozoic Era lasted from about 248 million years ago until about 65 million years ago. Some scientists think that during this time the **continents** which we know today separated from **Laurasia** and **Gondwanaland**. The Mesozoic Era contains the **Triassic**, the **Jurassic** and the **Cretaceous** periods.
Many reptiles lived on the Earth during the Mesozoic Era.

metal *noun*
A metal is a kind of **element**. About three-quarters of all elements are metals. Unlike other elements, metals can conduct **heat** and electricity. Metals combine with **oxygen** to make **compounds** called **oxides**.
Gold, tin and aluminium are all metals.

metallurgist *noun*
A metallurgist is a scientist who studies **metallurgy**.
The metallurgist tested the iron ore for purity.

metallurgy *noun*
Metallurgy is the study of metals and their **alloys**. In metallurgy, scientists examine the physical and **chemical** properties of metals.
The study of metallurgy is important in the motor industry.

metamorphic *adjective*
Metamorphic describes one of the three main kinds of **rock** or **stone**. The other kinds are **igneous** and **sedimentary** rock. The structure of metamorphic rocks has been changed by heat, high **pressure** or water. Metamorphic rocks are usually harder than the rocks from which they were formed.
Schist, gneiss, slate and marble are all metamorphic rocks.

meteorite *noun*
A meteorite is a piece of solid **mineral** from space which lands on the surface of the **Earth**. Meteorites contain large amounts of **silica**, **nickel** and **iron**.
The meteorite made a deep pit when it landed in the field.

meteorograph *noun*
A meteorograph is an instrument. It is used by **meteorologists** to record information about the Earth's **atmosphere**. It is attached to a balloon and floats in the **stratosphere**.
The meteorograph floated higher in the atmosphere than any aeroplane.

meteorologist *noun*
A meteorologist is a scientist who studies **meteorology**. Meteorologists can predict changes in the **weather** and make **weather forecasts**.
The meteorologist said that it would rain later.

meteorology *noun*
Meteorology is the study of the **atmosphere** and **weather** of the **Earth**.
The scientist used her knowledge of meteorology to explain the climate.

methane *noun*

Methane is a **gas**. It is made of **carbon** and **hydrogen** and is formed when **organic** substances decompose. It is sometimes called marsh gas. **Natural gas** is mostly methane.

The methane burned with a clear flame.

mica *noun*

Mica is a kind of **mineral**. Mica has a smooth texture and breaks easily into sheets. Mica contains **potassium**, **aluminium** and **silicon**.

The rock contained flaky deposits of mica.

mid-oceanic ridge *noun*

A mid-oceanic ridge is a long range of **mountains** on the **ocean** floor. The spread of the sea-floor creates new **oceanic crust** at the mid-oceanic ridges. There are mid-oceanic ridges in the north and south Atlantic oceans, and in the Indian Ocean.

The sea was not as deep over the mid-oceanic ridge.

millibar   **bar**

mine *noun*

A mine is a deep pit in the ground. Mines are dug to extract **coal**, **metals** and **minerals** such as diamonds. Some of the world's mines are very deep.

The mine had many underground tunnels which connected together.

mineral   page 92

mineral salt   **salt**

mineral water *noun*

Mineral water is water which comes from **springs** in the **Earth**. Different kinds of mineral water contain different mineral **salts**. A few types of mineral water are fizzy because they contain **carbon dioxide**. Mineral waters are sometimes used for treating illnesses such as rheumatism and arthritis.

They drank mineral water for their health.

mineralogist *noun*

A mineralogist is a scientist who studies **mineralogy**. Mining companies often ask mineralogists to test new mining sites.

The mineralogist tested the area to see how much metal it contained.

mineralogy *noun*

Mineralogy is the study of **minerals**. Mineralogy deals with the physical and **chemical** properties of minerals, such as their colour, **crystal** shape, hardness and **lustre**.

The book on mineralogy showed the different types of mineral.

mining *noun*

Mining is the process of taking **metals**, valuable stones and **minerals** from the Earth. Most mining is done with large machines, such as drills and diggers.

Mining can take place on the Earth's surface or under the ground.

mineral   *noun*
A mineral is an **inorganic chemical** found in
the **earth** or in **rocks**. Most minerals are
made up of **crystals**, and many of them are
hard.
They dug a mine in the hillside to extract the
minerals.

claystone

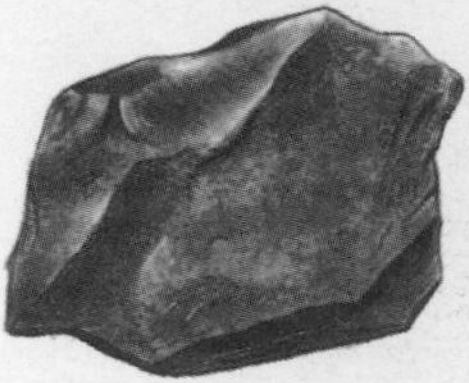

quartz

granite

slate

feldspar

hematite

pyrite

marble

fluorite

calcite

mica

sandstone

dolomite

Miocene *adjective*
Miocene describes an **epoch** in **geological time**. The Miocene Epoch occurred in the **Tertiary** sub-era and lasted from about 24 and a half million years ago to about 5 million years ago. Some scientists think that a human-like creature first appeared during the Miocene Epoch.
Many of today's species of mammal lived on the Earth during the Miocene Epoch.

Mississippian *adjective*
Mississippian describes a sub-period in **geological time**. It is the term used in North America for the most recent part of the **Carboniferous** Period. It lasted from about 360 million years ago to about 320 million years ago.
There was much volcanic activity during the Mississippian sub-period.

mist *noun*
Mist is tiny drops of **water** suspended in the air. When **clouds** form at ground level, it is called mist. Mist is difficult to see through. It is thicker than **haze**, but it is not as thick as **fog**.
We could not see the rocks because of the mist.

mistral *noun*
The mistral is the name of a strong, cool, dry **wind**. It blows from the Alps across southern France towards the Mediterranean Sea. The mistral can blow at up to 60 kilometres per hour. It usually blows in **winter**.
The grape harvest was damaged by the cold mistral.

moisture *noun*
Moisture is the amount of water **vapour** in the air or on a surface. Dry air contains very little moisture. A high moisture level can lead to the formation of **clouds**. The amount of water vapour in the air is also called **humidity**.
It was a cloudy day because the moisture level was so high.
moist *adjective*

molten *adjective*
Molten describes solids which have been heated above their melting point and have turned to liquid. **Magma** is molten rock. The **outer core**, deep inside the **Earth**, is also molten.
The molten rock came out of the erupting volcano as lava.

molten lava   erupting volcano

molybdenum *noun*
Molybdenum is an **element**. Pure molybdenum is a grey, silvery **metal**. Molybdenum is found as an **ore**, combined with **sulphur**. It has a very high melting point, so it is used as a heat-resistant material.
The molybdenum was used in steel alloys.

monsoon *noun*
A monsoon is a kind of **wind** which brings heavy rain. Monsoons occur in **tropical** regions and mark the change from the dry to the wet **season**.
The monsoon brought very heavy rain that washed away the crops.

moonstone *noun*
Moonstone is a kind of semi-precious stone. It has pale, shiny **crystals** and is often used in jewellery. Moonstone is a form of the mineral **feldspar**.
The moonstone shone in the candlelight.

moor *noun*

A moor is an area of high, open land where shrubs, such as heather, grow. Moors are found mainly in regions with a damp, **temperate** climate, such as north-west Europe. The soil contains much **peat**.
The footpath took us right over the moor.

moraine *noun*

Moraine is a word which describes the **rocks** and **gravel** carried along by a **glacier**. When a glacier melts, the moraine is left behind as small mounds and hills. These are also called moraines.
The ground was very stony because the field was on a moraine.

mountain *noun*

A mountain is a piece of land which is much higher than the surrounding countryside. Mountains usually have steep sides and sharp or rounded **peaks**. Mountains are higher than **hills**. High mountains always have snow at the top.
We climbed up from the lowlands to the highest mountain in the chain.

mountain chain *noun*

A mountain chain is a series of mountains connected together. The Pyrenees form a mountain chain between France and Spain
They could see the peaks of the mountain chain in the distance.

mountain range ▶ mountain chain

mouth *noun*

The mouth is the part of a river where the water flows out into the sea or a lake. The mouth of a cave is the entrance.
They played on the beach by the mouth of the river.

mud *noun*

Mud is a mixture of **clay**, **silt** and water. Mud is found at the bottom of rivers, lakes and **estuaries**. The **soil** of fields turns to mud after heavy rain. Many animals live in mud and some water plants are rooted in mud.
The mud on the road made it hard to drive.

mud flat *noun*

A mud flat is a piece of land near the **sea-shore** which is covered by the sea at high **tide**. A mud flat is made up of **silt** or **clay**. It contains **channels** which are made by the sea when it runs back through the mud.
He saw many birds feeding on the mud flat.

mudstone *noun*

Mudstone is a kind of **sedimentary** rock or **stone**. Mudstones are made of **clay** and **silt**.
There were mudstones along the sides of the quarry.

N

natural   *adjective*
Natural describes something which has not been made or altered by the activities of people. Natural vegetation describes plants which have not been disturbed by people or by farmed animals.
There was natural forest in the valley.
nature   *noun*

natural gas   *noun*
Natural gas is a mixture of **gases**. Natural gas is very often found under the ground with deposits of **crude oil**. Natural gas contains mainly **methane** and small amounts of other **hydrocarbons**. It is a **fossil fuel**.
They used natural gas to heat their house.

natural resource   *noun*
A natural resource is any useful substance found naturally. **Fossil fuels**, such as **coal**, **oil** and **natural gas**, are examples of natural resources. **Forests** are a natural resource and are used as a source of timber. Many natural resources need to be used carefully so that they are not used up.
The underground oil field was a valuable natural resource.

naturalist   *noun*
A naturalist is someone who studies the wild plants and animals of a region.
The naturalists studied the rain forest.

nautical   *adjective*
Nautical describes anything to do with ships, sailors or **navigation**.
They fitted the ship with the most modern nautical equipment.

navigation   *noun*
Navigation is a word which describes how a ship or boat is guided across the sea, a plane through the skies, or a vehicle along roads.
They missed the port that night because their navigation was bad.

neap tide   *noun*
A neap tide is a **tide** with a small difference in water level between high tide and low tide. Neap tides occur when the **gravities** of the Sun and the Moon pull in different directions. Neap tides occur about every 14 days.
The opposite of a neap tide is a **spring tide**.
Currents are weaker during neap tides.

neck ▶ plug

needle   *noun*
A needle is a pointed piece of rock rising up from the sea. Needles are found close to sea **cliffs**, but separate from the cliffs. A needle is also the name for a mass of rock standing alone on a mountain.
Many sea birds nested on the needle.

nekton   *noun*
Nekton describes all those animals which can swim freely in the open sea. Animals of the nekton do not drift with the **tides** and **currents**, unlike the **plankton**. They can move in any direction. They range in size from a few millimetres long to many metres long. The nekton does not include the animals of the **benthos**.
Fish make up a large part of the nekton.

neon *noun*
Neon is a colourless **gas**. It is found in very small amounts in the **atmosphere**. It is an **inert** gas so it does not easily form **compounds** with other **chemicals**. Neon is used to fill some kinds of electric light bulb.
The street was lit by lamps filled with neon.

nephrite *noun*
Nephrite is a **mineral**. Nephrite contains **silica** and can be found in a variety of colours including black, white, yellow and green. One form of **jade** comes from nephrite.
The jeweller used nephrite to make a ring.

neutral *adjective*
Neutral describes a substance which is neither an **acid** nor an **alkali**. Pure water is neutral, and so is normal soil. Many plants will only grow well on neutral soil.
The farmer put lime on the acid soil to make it neutral.

névé *noun*
Névé is a kind of **snow**. Névé is recent snow which does not melt. The snow gradually turns to **ice** as it builds up on the ground. Névé is found high up on mountains or on snowfields in the **polar** regions.
The névé on the glacier turned slowly into ice.

nickel *noun*
Nickel is an **element**. It is a **metal** that is found in many **ores**. Nickel is used to make many different **alloys**. The **core** of the Earth contains large amounts of nickel.
The alloy of nickel was harder than iron.

nimbostratus *adjective*
Nimbostratus describes a kind of **cloud**. A nimbostratus cloud forms high up and looks like a dark grey sheet across the sky. Nimbostratus clouds cover the Sun and often produce continuous rain or snow.
The nimbostratus clouds hid the Sun.

nitrogen *noun*
Nitrogen is the most common **gas** in the **atmosphere**. It makes up about 78 per cent of the air. Nitrogen is necessary for the growth of animals and plants. **Compounds** of nitrogen are used as **fertilizers**.
The farmer spread nitrogen on the fields to make them fertile.

noble ▶ **inert**

nodule *noun*
A nodule is a piece of hard **rock** which is found in softer, **sedimentary** rock. Nodules are also found on some parts of the sea-bed. These nodules are rich in iron and **manganese** ores.
Many nodules have been found on the floor of the Pacific Ocean.

nodules

non- *prefix*
Non- is a prefix that changes the meaning of the original word to the opposite meaning.
Carbon and oxygen are non-metallic elements because they are not metals.

non-ferrous *adjective*
Non-ferrous describes substances which do not contain **iron**. **Aluminium** is a non-ferrous metal but steel is not.
The machine was made of non-ferrous metal.

non-porous   *adjective*
Non-porous describes substances which do
not let water through. Hard rocks which do not
have cracks or gaps in them are non-porous.
Solid **clay** is also non-porous. The opposite of
non-porous is **porous**.
The non-porous rocks held water in a hollow.

non-renewable   *adjective*
Non-renewable describes **natural resources**
which cannot be replaced once they have
been used. **Oil** and **coal** are non-renewable
fossil fuels. **Wood** is renewable, if trees are
planted to replace those that are cut down.
*People are learning to conserve the Earth's
non-renewable resources.*

North Pole   *noun*
The North Pole is the most northern point
on the **Earth**. There are two north poles.
These are the geographical North Pole and
the **magnetic pole**.
*The North Pole is about 1,760 kilometres from
the magnetic north pole.*

northern hemisphere   *noun*
The northern hemisphere is the half of the
Earth which lies to the north of the **Equator**.
North America, Europe and Asia lie in the
northern hemisphere.
*The plane from Australia crossed the Equator
into the northern hemisphere.*

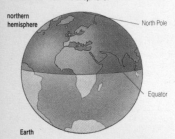

northern
hemisphere — North Pole

Equator

Earth

O

oasis   *noun*
An oasis is a **fertile** area with a good water
supply in a **desert**. An oasis may be a very
small area around a **spring**, or it may cover
a whole valley floor. The water in an oasis
allows trees and crops to grow.
We crossed the desert and reached the oasis.

desert
spring
fertile area

obsidian   *noun*
Obsidian is a kind of **rock**. It is an **igneous**
rock with a **glass**-like texture.
*The rocks near the volcano contained
patches of glassy obsidian.*

ocean   *noun*
An ocean is a very large **sea**. There are five
oceans. These are the Pacific, Atlantic,
Indian, Arctic and Southern oceans. Together,
the oceans cover 71 per cent of the Earth's
surface.
The ship took many days to cross the ocean.

ocean basin   *noun*
The ocean basin is part of the **ocean floor**
in areas where the **ocean** is more than
2,000 metres deep. It is the gently sloping or
flat part of the floor between **oceanic ridges**.
*The underwater mountain sloped down
towards the ocean basin.*

ocean current *noun*
An ocean current is a regular movement of
sea water in the surface of the seas or
oceans. Ocean currents follow particular
routes. The Gulf Stream, which flows
northwards in the Atlantic Ocean, is an
example of an ocean current.
*The boats were helped on their way by the
strong ocean current.*

ocean floor ► page 100

oceanic climate ► **maritime**

oceanic crust *noun*
The oceanic crust is the inner and denser
part of the Earth's **crust**. It lies beneath the
oceans, but also partly continues beneath
the **continents**. The oceanic crust is about
5 kilometres thick. It is made largely of **sima**.
*The rocks below the oceans form part of the
oceanic crust.*

oceanic ridge *noun*
An oceanic ridge is an underwater **range** of
mountains. The ridges wind their way around
the **ocean floor** for many thousands of
kilometres. Most mountains in the oceanic
ridges stand about 1,500 metres above the
ocean floor. The best known oceanic ridge is
the Mid-Atlantic Ridge in the Atlantic Ocean.
*The bed of the ocean rose up sharply towards
the oceanic ridge.*

oceanographer *noun*
An oceanographer studies the **oceans** of
the world. Some oceanographers study the
physical and **chemical** properties of the
oceans. Others study the **biological** life of
the oceans.
*The oceanographer explained how the ocean
currents move chemicals around in the seas.*

oceanography *noun*
Oceanography is the study of everything to do
with **oceans**.
*By studying oceanography, she became an
expert in marine life.*

offshore *adjective*
Offshore describes something which moves
away from the **sea-shore** or which is out to
sea. An offshore **breeze** is a breeze blowing
away from the sea-shore. It blows away from
the land and out to sea. The opposite of
offshore is **onshore**.
*The sailing boat picked up speed in the
offshore wind.*

oil *noun*
Oil is a kind of **fossil fuel**. Oil is a thick, dark
liquid which is made of **hydrocarbons**. It was
formed over millions of years from the
remains of plants. **Crude oil** is usually found
underground with **natural gas** and solid
hydrocarbons. Oil can also be extracted from
some forms of shale and sand. An area
containing reserves of oil is called an **oil field**.
Oil and oil products are sometimes called
petroleum.
*The well pumped up the oil from deep
underground to the surface.*

oil field ► page 104

Oligocene *adjective*
Oligocene describes an **epoch** in **geological
time**. It is one of the epochs of the **Tertiary**
sub-era. The Oligocene Epoch lasted from
about 38 million years ago until about 24 and
a half million years ago.
*Some scientists think that the first apes
appeared on Earth during the Oligocene
Epoch.*

ocean floor *noun*
The ocean floor is the name given to the
bottom of the **oceans**. The deepest part of the
ocean floor is called the **abyssal plain**. From
the abyssal plain, the ocean floor rises
upwards towards the **continents**. The ocean
floor is made of rocks, covered by layers
of mud.
The wrecked ship sank down through the
water until it rested on the ocean floor.

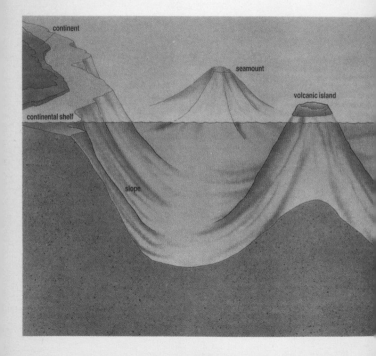

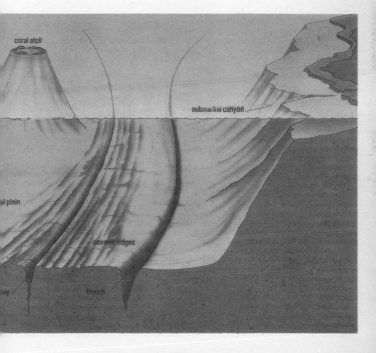

coral atoll

submarine canyon

al plain

oceanic ridges

ey

trench

onshore *adjective*
Onshore describes something which is at the
sea-shore or which moves towards the
sea-shore. An onshore **breeze** is a breeze
blowing towards the sea-shore from the sea.
The opposite of onshore is **offshore**.
*The strong onshore wind quickly blew the
boat into the port.*

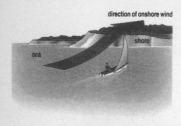

direction of onshore wind

shore

sea

onyx *noun.*
Onyx is a **mineral**. It is a form of **chalcedony**
that contains **opal**. Onyx is a semi-precious
stone and is similar to **agate**.
*His ring contained a brown and white onyx
stone.*

ooze *noun*
Ooze is a kind of slimy **sediment** found on the
ocean floor. Ooze is made of the remains of
plankton, animals and plants mixed with **clay**
and **silt**.
*The submarine collected samples of the ooze
at the bottom of the sea.*

opal *noun*
Opal is a **mineral**. An opal is a form of **silica**
and a semi-precious stone. Opals can be
white or they may have **rainbow** colours.
Some of the finest opals come from Australia.
The ring had an opal at its centre.

opisometer *noun*
An opisometer is an instrument for measuring
distances on a **map**. An opisometer has a
wheel which traces a line on the map. The
wheel is attached to a **scale** which measures
the distance that the wheel has travelled.
*He used an opisometer to measure how far
they had walked.*

orbit *noun*
An orbit is the path followed by an object as
it circles another object in space. The Earth
follows an orbit around the Sun. Satellites
and space stations circle the Earth in orbits.
*The spaceship followed an orbit around the
Earth.*

Ordovician *adjective*
Ordovician describes a **period** in **geological
time**. The Ordovician Period lasted from
about 505 million years ago until about
438 million years ago.
*The geologist showed us a fossil coral from
the Ordovician Period.*

ore *noun*
An ore is a kind of **mineral**. An ore contains
useful **metals**, such as **gold**, **tin** or **iron**.
Pure metals can be **extracted** from large
quantities of ore.
*The train brought many loads of iron ore to the
foundry.*

organic   *adjective*
Organic describes a group of chemical **compounds**. Organic **chemicals** are those which contain atoms of **carbon**. Organic chemicals are often composed of carbon atoms joined together in chains or rings. All living things are made of organic chemicals. The opposite of organic is **inorganic**.
The biologist explained that animals and plants contain organic compounds.

osmium   *noun*
Osmium is an **element**. It is a hard, brittle **metal** which has a bluish-white colour. It is similar to **platinum** and is often found in the same ores as platinum.
They used osmium to make the hard tips of the pen nibs.

outcrop   *noun*
An outcrop is an area of land where the **bedrock** comes to the surface. An outcrop may be of exposed rocks, or it may be covered with soil and plants.
He noticed different flowers growing on the limestone outcrop.

outer core   *noun*
The outer core is part of the interior of the **Earth**. It lies inside the **mantle**, about 2,300 kilometres below the surface of the Earth. The outer core is very hot. It is thought to be made of **molten** rocks, with large amounts of **nickel** and iron. Inside the outer core lies the **inner core**.
The map of the inside of the Earth showed the position of the outer core.

ox-bow lake   *noun*
An ox-bow lake is a shallow **lake** found beside a **river**. Ox-bow lakes are curved in shape. They form at a deep **meander** or bend in a river. When the river changes its course, the meander silts up and forms an ox-bow lake. In North America, ox-bow lakes are called bayous.
The ox-bow lake was almost overgrown with water plants.

oxide   *noun*
An oxide is a chemical **compound**. An oxide forms when an **element** reacts with **oxygen**. Iron reacts with oxygen in the air to make iron oxide, or rust.
The car's exhaust gave out poisonous oxides.

oxygen   *noun*
Oxygen is an **element**. It is a common, colourless **gas**. One-fifth of the Earth's **atmosphere** is oxygen. Oxygen is the most common element in the Earth's **crust**. Nearly all living things need oxygen to survive.
The waterweed was covered in bubbles of oxygen.

ozone   *noun*
Ozone is a **compound** and a colourless **gas**. Ozone is a type of **oxygen**. It is formed when oxygen is exposed to **radiation**, especially in the upper **atmosphere**. Ozone is poisonous to breathe in large quantities.
The scientists measured the amount of ozone in the air.

ozone layer   *noun*
The ozone layer is the name for part of the Earth's **atmosphere**. It is about 22 kilometres above the Earth's surface and is part of the **stratosphere**. The ozone layer protects the Earth from the harmful **radiation** of the Sun. Certain **gases** called chlorofluorocarbons, or CFCs, may damage the ozone layer.
The chemicals that collected in the air began to make the ozone layer thinner.

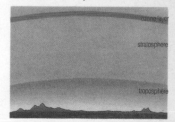

103

oil field *noun*

An oil field is the name given to a large underground **deposit** of **crude oil**. Oil fields are found in **sedimentary rocks**, often thousands of metres below the surface of the Earth. There are large oil fields in the Middle East and in the United States of America. *They drilled through the rocks to reach the oil in the oil field.*

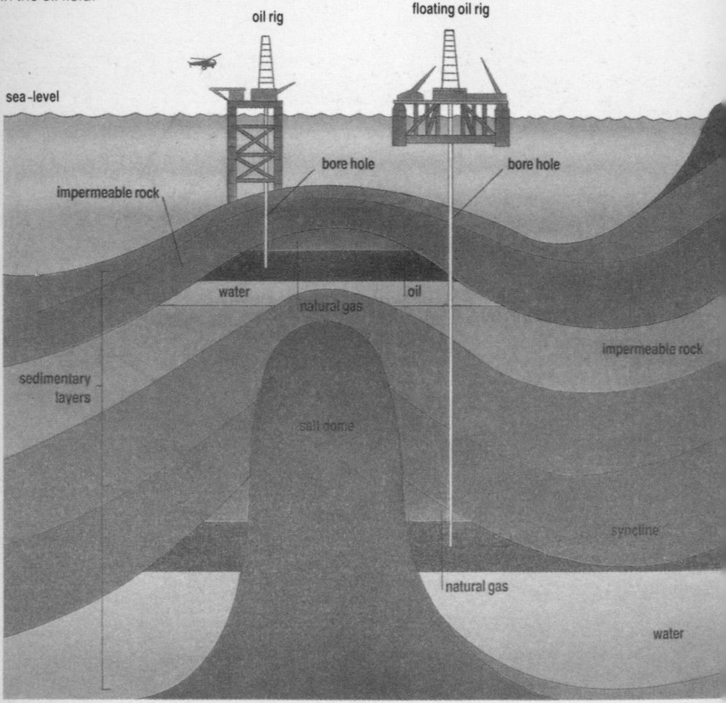

oil rig

floating oil rig

sea-level

bore hole

bore hole

impermeable rock

water

oil

natural gas

impermeable rock

sedimentary layers

salt dome

syncline

natural gas

water

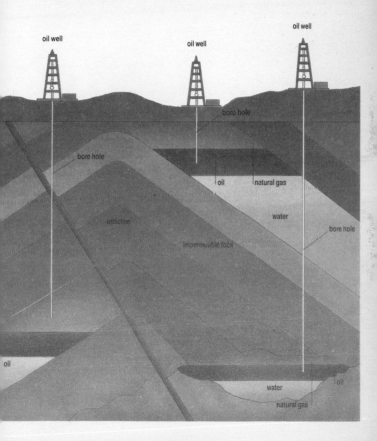

P

paleo-   *prefix*
Paleo- is a prefix meaning old or ancient.
The science of paleontology tells us about life in the distant past.

Paleocene   *adjective*
Paleocene describes one of the **epochs** of the **Tertiary** sub-era. The Paleocene Epoch lasted from about 65 million years ago until about 55 million years ago.
The Paleocene Epoch comes at the start of the Tertiary sub-era.

paleogeography   *noun*
Paleogeography is the study of the **geography** of the Earth in earlier **geological time**. A student of paleogeography tries to work out what the Earth was like millions of years ago, by studying **fossils** and **rocks**.
He learnt more about paleogeography by closely examining the fossils.

paleontologist   *noun*
A paleontologist is someone who studies **fossils**. Some paleontologists collect and describe fossils. Others use the fossil traces left by extinct animals and plants to help them reconstruct the animal or plant.
The paleontologist showed me her collection of fossils.

paleontology   *noun*
Paleontology is the study of **fossils**. Paleontology can also be the study of the processes in **geology** which led to the formation of the fossils.
He studied paleontology to learn more about fossils.

Paleozoic   *adjective*
Paleozoic describes one of the **eras** in **geological time**. The Paleozoic Era lasted from about 590 million years ago until about 248 million years ago.
In the middle of the Paleozoic Era, the first land plants appeared.

pampas   *noun*
The pampas is a kind of **grassland**. The pampas is found in South America, mainly in Uruguay and Argentina. There are many tall grasses on the pampas and trees are scarce.
The farmer led his cattle out onto the pampas.

Pangaea ▶ page 108

panning   *noun*
Panning describes a simple method used for separating precious **metals** from **gravel**. Panning is mostly used to search for **gold**. A person panning for gold sieves the gravel of a **stream** or **river** and then picks out any pieces of gold by hand.
She used panning to collect a handful of gold from the stream.

sieve

precious metal ———   ——— gravel

Panthalassa *noun*
Panthalassa is the name of the large **ocean** which some scientists believe surrounded the **super-continent** of **Pangaea**. Panthalassa may have existed between about 250 million years ago and 215 million years ago.
The map showed us the position of the huge sea called Panthalassa.

parallel *noun*
A parallel is another name for a line of **latitude**.
The ship sailed across several parallels as it travelled north.

pass *noun*
A pass is a narrow path or channel. It is usually an area of lower ground through **hills** or **mountains**. A pass connects one **valley** with another valley.
They climbed over the pass and then walked down into the valley beyond.

peak *noun*
A peak is the highest point of a **mountain**. Some mountains have several peaks close together. Other mountains have a single peak. Mount Everest, in the Himalayas in Asia, rises to a peak at a height of 8,848 metres above **sea-level**.
We could see the peak of the mountain rising above the clouds.

peat *noun*
Peat is a kind of **soil**. It is made from the decomposing remains of plants, mainly mosses, and has a dark brown colour. Peat develops under wet conditions in **bogs**. Peat is a very good source of **humus**. It can also be dried and burned as a **fuel**.
Sphagnum moss is one of the most important plants that form peat.

pebble *noun*
A pebble is a small piece of **rock**. Pebbles are rounded. They are often found on **beaches**. Pebbles are between about 4 millimetres and 6 millimetres across.
We found it hard to walk across the pebbles.

pedology *noun*
Pedology is the study of **soils**. It includes studying how different kinds of soil are made, and what the soils are made from. Pedology also involves making **maps** of different soils to show where they are found.
They studied pedology to find out about the soils in the area.

pelagic *adjective*
Pelagic describes substances or life found in the open water of the **sea** or in a large **lake**. Pelagic fish are those which spend their lives swimming in the open sea or in the surface waters. Pelagic animals include the **nekton** and the **plankton**, but not the **benthos**.
The fishing boat put out a net near the surface to catch pelagic fish.

Pangaea *noun*

Pangaea is the name of a very large land mass, or **super-continent**, which some scientists think existed about 250 million years ago. They think it broke up about 215 million years ago and that the continents moved slowly apart.

All the land in the world may have been joined together in the super-continent of Pangaea.

Triassic Period
Before 215 million
years ago

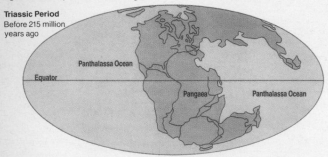

Jurassic Period
After 215 million
years ago

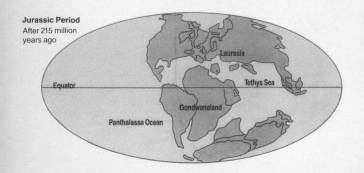

Cretaceous Period
Before 65 million
years ago

Holocene Epoch
Present day

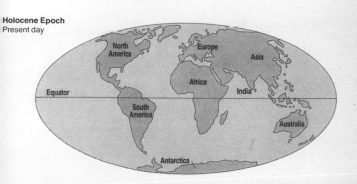

peneplain *noun*
A peneplain is a kind of fairly flat **plain**. In a peneplain, the rocks are very old and have been worn away by millions of years of **erosion**. Some of the best developed peneplains are found in southern Africa and in Brazil.
The old rocks formed part of an ancient peneplain.

peninsula *noun*
A peninsula is a narrow area of **land** which stretches out into the sea or into a **lake**. A peninsula can be small, or very large like the Malay peninsula in South-east Asia.
From the top of the peninsula, she could see the sea on both sides.

South China Sea
Malaysia
Singapore

Pennsylvanian *adjective*
Pennsylvanian describes a sub-period in **geological time**. The Pennsylvanian sub-period is the name given in North America to the later part of the **Carboniferous** Period. It lasted from 320 million years ago to 286 million years ago.
Coal began to form during the Pennsylvanian sub-period.

peridot *noun*
Peridot, or olivine, is a **mineral**. It is made of **silica**, **iron** and **magnesium**. Peridot is hard and glassy, with an olive-green colour. Good **crystals** of peridot are used as **gems**.
The stones included some pale green crystals of peridot.

peridotite *noun*
Peridotite is an **igneous** rock. It has a very coarse grain. Peridotite is very common in the Earth's **mantle** and often contains the mineral **peridot**.
The rock in the area contained peridotite.

period *noun*
A period is one of the main divisions of **geological time**. Each **era** is divided into several periods. The oldest period began 590 million years ago. Each period is divided into **epochs**.
Coal formed in the Carboniferous Period.

periodic table *noun*
The periodic table is a list of all the **elements**. In the periodic table, the elements are listed in order, from the lightest to the heaviest atomic weights.
Hydrogen is the element with the lowest atomic weight in the periodic table.

permafrost *noun*
Permafrost describes **ground** which is always frozen. Permafrost occurs in regions which are very cold, such as the **Arctic**. In the Arctic **summer**, the **ice** on the surface of the ground melts. The ground below is still frozen. The soil gets very wet because permafrost below stops the water draining away.
We could not dig because of the permafrost.

permeable *adjective*
Permeable describes something through which **water** can pass. A permeable **soil** is a soil which allows free **drainage** of water. The opposite of permeable is **impermeable**.
The limestone rock was very permeable.

Permian *adjective*
Permian describes a **period** in geological time. The Permian Period lasted from about 286 million years ago to about 248 million years ago. The Permian Period is the first period of the **Paleozoic** Era.
Ammonites lived during the Permian Period.

pervious *adjective*
Pervious describes **rocks** through which water slowly passes. Water passes through a pervious rock by seeping along cracks and joints. Some limestone and some igneous rocks are pervious. The opposite of pervious is **impervious**.
The water dripped into the cave through the pervious rocks above.

petrified forest *noun*
A petrified forest is a **forest** which has been turned into **fossils**. The wood in the trees is gradually replaced by **silica** from water which is rich in mineral **salts**. The most famous example is in the Petrified Forest National Park in the United States of America.
They saw stone-like fossil trees in the petrified forest.

fossil trees

petroleum ▶ oil

petrologist *noun*
A petrologist is a scientist who studies **rocks**. Petrologists identify different rocks from their structure and from the **chemicals** of which they are made. They also study the geological processes which make different types of rock.
The petrologist explained how he knew that the rock was granite.
petrology *noun*

Phanerozoic *adjective*
Phanerozoic describes the most recent **eon** in **geological time**. It began about 590 million years ago and continues today.
All the geological periods have occurred during the Phanerozoic Eon.

phosphorus *noun*
Phosphorus is an **element**. It is found in many different types of **rock** and **mineral**, mainly as a **compound** with **calcium**. Phosphorus is used to make matches and **fertilizers**. All living things need phosphorus.
The crops were unhealthy because there was not enough phosphorus in the soil.

physical geography *noun*
Physical geography is the study of the surface of **continents** and of **landscapes**. It includes looking at the way the landscape is formed. This can be by **erosion**, the flow of rivers or **glaciation**.
The physical geography of the valley showed that it had once been filled with thick ice.

physical map *noun*
A physical map is a **map** which shows details of the physical **features** of the **landscape**. A physical map can show any low and high ground, **rivers**, **lakes** and **marshes**.
She looked at the physical map to see where the mountains lay.

piedmont *noun*
A piedmont is a gentle **slope** running down from a **mountain** to a **plain**. A piedmont is found at the foot of a mountain.
They came down from the foothills onto a broad piedmont.

piedmont

pipe *noun*
A pipe is a tube-shaped opening in a solid substance. A pipe is the **vent** through which **lava** rises into the **crater** of a **volcano**. The word can also describe a hole in rock which is filled with a different rock or **mineral**.
The geologist found diamonds in a pipe.

pitchblende *noun*
Pitchblende is an **ore** of **uranium**. It is very
radioactive and has a black colour. Uranium
and **radium** can be obtained from
pitchblende.
Radium was first extracted from pitchblende.

plain *noun*
A plain is a flat area of **lowlands**. Many plains
stretch for hundreds of kilometres. The plains
of East Africa are covered with trees and
grasslands. The Great Plains of North
America are used for growing grain crops.
*The grassland stretched away across the
open plain.*

planet *noun*
A planet is a large mass which travels around
the **Sun**. There are nine planets in our **solar**
system. The **Earth** is the third closest planet
to the Sun and takes one year to travel around
it. Planets can be made of **rocks** or **gases**.
The Earth is made of rocks and is surrounded
by an **atmosphere**.
*The Earth is the only planet known to support
living things.*

plankton *noun*
Plankton is the name for the tiny animals and
plants that float in the **water** or in the **air**. They
cannot control their movements, but drift
along on **currents**. Marine plankton are found
in the upper layers of the sea. Aerial plankton
include tiny insects and spiders which get
swept up in air currents. Many plankton can
only be seen with a microscope.
The fish fed on the plankton in the sea.

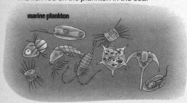

marine plankton

plate ► tectonic plate

plate tectonics *noun*
Plate tectonics is the study of movements in
the Earth's **crust**. The crust is thought to be
divided into a number of **tectonic plates**
which move and push against each other.
There are seven large plates and twelve
smaller ones. One plate can move under
another in a **subduction zone**. Plates can
move apart, and **sea-floor spreading** will
occur. The plates can also slide past each
other without any change to their size.
*The study of plate tectonics shows that the
continents are slowly moving.*

plateau (plural **plateaux**) *noun*
A plateau is a raised area of flattish ground.
A plateau is surrounded by steep **slopes** or
escarpments. Most plateaux lie above
600 metres. The Tibetan plateau lies at a
height of about 4,000 metres.
*The village was built overlooking the edge of
a high plateau.*

escarpment

plateau

platinum *noun*
Platinum is an **element**. It is a silvery **metal**.
Platinum is normally found combined with
sulphur. It is rare and valuable, and used
to make jewellery.
He wore a shiny ring of platinum.

Pleistocene *adjective*
Pleistocene describes an **epoch** in
geological time. It occurred in the
Quaternary sub-era and lasted from about
2 million years ago to about 10,000 years ago.
*Many glaciations took place during the
Pleistocene Epoch.*

Pliocene *adjective*
Pliocene describes an **epoch** in **geological time**. It is the last epoch in the **Tertiary** sub-era and lasted from about 5 million years ago to about 2 million years ago.
Ice-caps developed during the Pliocene Epoch.

plug *noun*
A plug is a mass of solid **lava** in the **vent** of a **volcano** which is **dormant** or **extinct**. Sometimes, a plug is left exposed when the softer rock surrounding it erodes away.
The castle was built high up on an old plug.

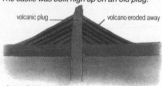
volcanic plug ———   volcano eroded away

plutonium *noun*
Plutonium is an **element**. It is not found naturally as an **ore**. Plutonium is **radioactive** and is made in nuclear reactors from **uranium**. Plutonium is mainly used as a **nuclear fuel**.
The waste from the nuclear reactor contained high levels of plutonium.

polar *adjective*
Polar describes something which comes from or which is found close to the **North Pole** or **South Pole**. Polar air is cold air moving from the polar regions.
The explorers set out to cross the polar ice.

pole *noun*
The poles of the Earth are the points at its extreme north or south. The **North Pole** and the **South Pole** are directly opposite each other. They are known as the geographical poles. The North Pole is over the frozen **Arctic** Ocean. The South Pole is over the ice-covered **continent** of **Antarctica**.
They walked across the ice to reach the pole.

pollute *verb*
To pollute is to add **impurities** or unwanted substances, especially to the **environment**. Untreated sewage can pollute **rivers**. Factories may pollute the **atmosphere** with smoke and the water with waste **chemicals**. **Acid rain** pollutes land and water.
The oil spill polluted the sea over a wide area.
pollution *noun*

polonium *noun*
Polonium is an **element**. It is a **metal** which is **radioactive**. Polonium is found naturally with **uranium** in **pitchblende**.
The scientists measured the radioactivity of the polonium.

porcelain *noun*
Porcelain is a hard, white substance. Porcelain is made from kaolin, **feldspar** and **quartz**, which are heated together at a high **temperature**. It is used to make objects such as cups and saucers.
He carefully washed the valuable porcelain.

porous *adjective*
Porous describes something through which water is able to pass. **Gravel** is very porous, and so are **soils** which contain a lot of **sand** or **organic** matter.
The porous soil dried out quickly after the heavy rain.

porphyry *noun*
Porphyry is a kind of **igneous** rock. Porphyry is any igneous rock which has large **crystals**.
The sculpture was chiselled out of porphyry.

projection   *noun*

Projection is a process used in **map**-making.
It is very difficult to draw a flat map of a round
world. Only one part of the map will be drawn
to a correct **scale**. Other areas of the map will
be stretched or reduced in size to fit. There
are different ways of altering the shapes to fit
the flat map. These are called projection.
*The projection used in the map made
Greenland seem as large as South America.*

cylindrical projection

Cylindrical projection fits a map onto a cylinder shape. The
scale of the map is correct along the Equator, but gets more
and more stretched as it approaches the poles. Cylindrical
projection is most often used for maps of areas on either side
of the Equator.

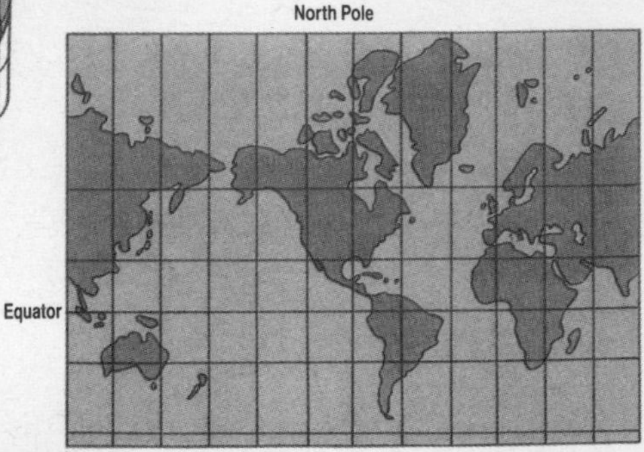

North Pole

Equator

conical projection

Conical projection fits a map onto a cone shape. The scale of the map is correct along the **meridians**, but only correct along one or two chosen lines of **latitude**. Conical projection is good for making maps of countries with large areas of land running east and west.

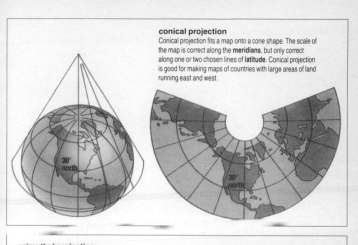

azimuthal projection

Azimuthal projection fits a map onto a flat shape. The scale of the map is correct where the flat shape and the curve of the Earth meet. Azimuthal projection can be used for mapping areas such as the poles.

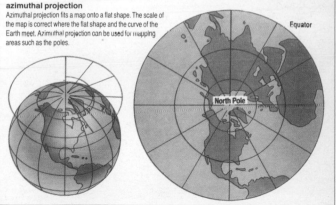

pot hole *noun*
A pot hole is a smooth-sided, round hole in the rocky bed of a **stream**. A pot hole forms when the water swirls **pebbles** around in a shallow dip. This gradually erodes the dip and it becomes a pot hole. A pot hole is also the name for the shaft where a stream runs into an underground limestone **cave**.
The stream flowed into a large pot hole.

potash *noun*
Potash is a **compound** of **potassium**. It is made of potassium carbonate and other potassium **salts**. Potash is found with other salts, such as common salt, in **salt lakes**. It is also found in ash. Potash is used as a **fertilizer** for plants.
We put potash on the garden soil to help the plants grow.

potassium *noun*
Potassium is an **element**. It is a **metal** which is found in many **minerals**, and also in sea water. All living things need some potassium to grow.
The cooking salt contained potassium.

prairie *noun*
The prairie is the treeless, grassy **plain** in the centre of the North American **continent**. On the prairie, the rain falls mostly in the **summer**, when it is also hot. In the **winter**, it is dry and cold.
We rode on horseback over the open prairie.

Precambrian *adjective*
Precambrian is a name sometimes used for the earliest part of **geological time**. It includes the **Priscoan**, **Archean** and **Proterozoic** eons. It lasted from about 4,600 million years ago until about 590 million years ago. Many ancient rocks date from Precambrian times.
The centre of the continent was made of Precambrian rocks.

precipitation *noun*
Precipitation is the **water** which falls from the **atmosphere** onto the Earth's surface. It includes **snow**, **sleet**, **hail** and **dew** as well as **rain**.
The ground was wet from the precipitation.

pressure *noun*
Pressure is the force of the **atmosphere** or **water** on the Earth. **Atmospheric pressure** is lower at the top of a mountain than at **sea-level**. Water pressure increases at lower and lower depths in the sea.
They thought the weather would change because the atmospheric pressure dropped suddenly.

pressure gradient *noun*
A pressure gradient is the difference in **pressure** between two points. There is a steep pressure gradient between an area of **high pressure** and one of **low pressure**. A steep pressure gradient, with strong winds, is marked on a weather chart by **isobars** placed close together. Widely-spaced isobars show a weak gradient and light winds.
The wind reached gale force as the pressure gradient rose.

prevailing wind *noun*
The prevailing wind in an area is the **wind** which blows there most often. At different seasons of the year, the direction of the prevailing wind may change.
The prevailing wind blew from the west.

prime meridian ▶ **Greenwich meridian**

Priscoan *adjective*
Priscoan is the name given to the earliest **eon** of **geological time**. Some scientists think that it dated from 4,600 million years ago to 4,000 million years ago. The Priscoan Eon is the earliest part of **Precambrian** time.
Some scientists think that the Earth was formed during the Priscoan Eon.

projection ► page 114

promontory ► **headland**

Proterozoic *adjective*
Proterozoic describes an **eon** in **geological time**. The Proterozoic Eon lasted from about 2,500 million years ago to about 590 million years ago. The Proterozoic Eon is the later part of **Precambrian** time.
Life first appeared in the sea during the Proterozoic Eon.

pumice *noun*
Pumice is a kind of **igneous** rock. It is very light because it has a sponge-like structure and is full of holes. Some pumice even floats on water. Pumice is a kind of **lava**. It is formed from frothy, **molten** rock which cooled down so quickly it did not form crystals. Pumice is used as an **abrasive**.
We found pieces of pumice near the volcano.

pyrite *noun*
Pyrite is a **mineral**. Crystals of pyrite are very shiny and have a gold colour. Pyrite is sometimes called fool's gold. It is made of **iron** and **sulphur** and is found in **sedimentary** and **igneous** rocks.
They mined the pyrite as a source of sulphur.

quagmire *noun*
A quagmire is an area of very soft, wet **ground**. It is difficult to walk on a quagmire because of the danger of sinking.
We had to take a different route to avoid the quagmire.

quarry *noun*
A quarry is an open pit made by digging for rocks or **minerals**. The surface soil is removed to reach the rocks or minerals below. Stone for building and **slate**, **sand** and **gravel** are dug from quarries.
The slates for the new roof came from the local quarry.

quartz *noun*
Quartz is a **mineral**. When it is pure, quartz is transparent and colourless. Quartz is made of **crystals** of **silica** and is hard enough to scratch glass. It is the most common mineral in the rocks of the Earth.
The pale quartz showed up clearly amongst the darker rocks.

Quaternary   *adjective*
Quaternary describes a sub-era in
geological time. The Quaternary sub-era is
the most recent of all geological time, and
includes the **Pleistocene** and **Holocene**
epochs. It began about 2 million years ago
and continues to the present day.
We are still living in the Quaternary sub-era.

quicksand   *noun*
Quicksand is very wet **sand**. Quicksand
becomes more liquid when it is pressed. It is
easy to sink into quicksand so it is dangerous
to walk over. Quicksand is found in some
estuaries.
*The farmer had to pull the cow out of the
quicksand with a rope.*

R

radiation   *noun*
Radiation is a kind of **energy**. It includes the
particles given off by **elements** which are
radioactive. Some radiation is harmful in
large doses and can destroy living cells.
*The nuclear power station had very thick
walls to contain the radiation.*

radioactive   *adjective*
Radioactive describes **elements** which
give off **radiation**. Some elements, such
as **uranium** and **radium**, are naturally
radioactive.
*The scientist worked out the age of the
radioactive rocks.*
radioactivity   *noun*

radium   *noun*
Radium is an **element**. It is a **metal** which is
radioactive . Radium is found in ores such as
pitchblende. Radium decays to form the gas
radon.
*The scientist used radium as a source of
radiation.*

radon   *noun*
Radon is an **inert** gas. It is found in small
quantities in the **atmosphere**. Radon is given
off when the metal **radium** decays.
*They had to move house because the rocks
below produced a high level of radon.*

rain   *noun*
Rain is **water** which falls in drops from
the **clouds**. The biggest raindrops fall
as **thunderstorms** or heavy showers.
The smallest drops are drizzle.
They were soon soaked by the heavy rain.

rain forest *noun*

A rain forest is a special kind of **forest** with tall trees and many climbing plants. Rain forests are found in **tropical** regions. Here, the climate is always warm and there is a high **rainfall**. Central America, South America, Africa and South-east Asia have many rain forests. The largest is the Amazon rain forest in South America.
They saw many animals in the rain forest, such as monkeys, snakes and parrots.

rainbow *noun*

A rainbow is an arch of colours seen in the sky. There are six main colours in a rainbow. These are red, orange, yellow, green, blue and violet. When **sunlight** shines through **rain**, the raindrops split up the sunlight into these colours.
She watched the rainbow appear in the sky over the fields.

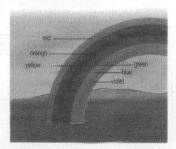

rainfall *noun*

Rainfall is the amount of **rain** that falls. It is usually measured in millimetres per year. Some parts of the world have a very high rainfall, which causes **floods**. In places where there is not enough rainfall, there may be a **drought**.
The heavy rainfall brought enormous floods, which caused widespread damage.

range *noun*

A range is a series of objects in a line, such as **mountains** or **hills**. Range is also used to describe open, rolling country, such as the **prairie** in North America.
The mountain range was covered in snow.

rapids *noun*

Rapids are very fast-flowing parts of a **river**. In the rapids, the **water** rushes quickly over a series of **waterfalls**.
The rapids made the river very dangerous.

rare earth *noun*

A rare earth is a kind of **element**. Rare earth elements are found in small quantities in **minerals**. Although they are called rare earths, some of these substances can be found quite easily.
The rock from the moors contained rare earths.

ravine *noun*

A ravine is a deep, narrow river **valley**. Ravines are formed when rivers rush over rocks and wear away a **channel**. A ravine is similar to a **gorge**, but the sides are not as steep.
He climbed carefully so that he did not fall down the ravine.

119

reef *noun*

A reef is a line of hard **rocks** or **coral** at or
near the surface of the sea. **Coral reefs** form
in warm water round volcanic **islands**. In
time, the volcano may disappear beneath the
water, and the reef may become an **atoll** with
a **lagoon** in the centre.
Reefs can be very dangerous to shipping.

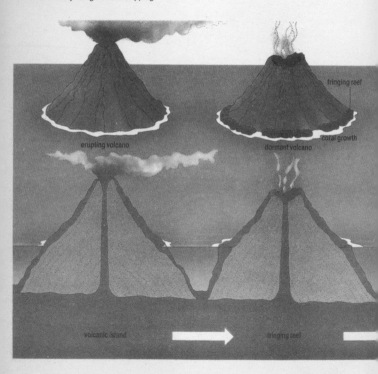

erupting volcano

dormant volcano

fringing reef

coral growth

volcanic island

fringing reef

The four stages of reef development are shown below. The top pictures show what the reefs look like above the water. The bottom pictures are a cross-section of the reefs. This shows what is happening under the water and inside the volcano or reef.

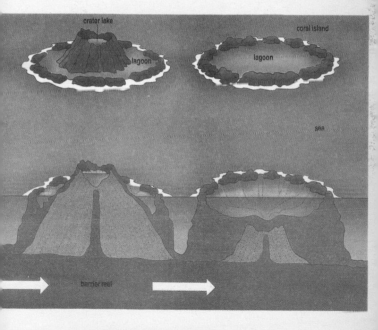

crater lake

coral island

lagoon

lagoon

sea

barrier reef

river *noun*

A river is a large stream of **water** which flows along a **channel** called a **river bed**. The **source** of a river is high in hills and mountains, usually at a spring or a lake. Rivers flow down towards the sea, collecting more water and growing wider and slower. *The longest rivers flow for thousands of kilometres.*

mountains

spring

rapids

tributary

waterfall

mouth

flood plain

estuary

delta

sea

red clay *noun*
Red clay is a kind of **clay** formed deep in the **oceans**. It is made up of fine particles which are carried by **ocean currents** to the deepest parts of the sea.
Red clay covers the deepest ocean floors.

reef ▶ page 120

reg *noun*
A reg is a kind of **desert**. It has a flat surface covered in **gravel**. Wind has swept away any small particles of loose **sand**.
There are many large areas of reg in the Sahara in North Africa.

region *noun*
A region is an area of **land**. Some regions are flat, while others are hilly. Each region has certain **features** which distinguish it from other regions nearby.
There were many lakes in the region.

relative humidity *noun*
Relative humidity is a measure of the amount of **moisture** in the **atmosphere**. If the relative humidity is very high, **mist**, **fog** or **rain** can occur. The relative humidity is usually lower during the day than during the night. It is measured using a **hygrometer**.
The fog was caused by the relative humidity.

relief map *noun*
A relief map is a **map** which shows the **features** of the **landscape**. The areas of high and low ground can be shown by **contours**, different colours or shading.
The relief map showed a range of hills.

reservoir *noun*
A reservoir is an artificial **lake**. Reservoirs store water which is used for drinking or for **irrigation**. Most reservoirs are made by stopping river water behind a **dam**. A deposit of **crude oil** can also be called a reservoir.
Our drinking water came from a reservoir.

resource ▶ **natural resource**

Richter Scale *noun*
The Richter Scale measures the strength of **earthquakes** and earth **tremors**. The Richter Scale goes from 0 to 9. Strong earthquakes measure over 7 on this scale.
The earthquake measured more than 6 points on the Richter Scale.

ridge *noun*
A ridge is a narrow, raised stretch of **land**. **Hills** and **mountains** which are close to each other are often joined together by a ridge.
There was a valley on each side of the ridge.

rift valley *noun*
A rift valley is a long, deep **valley**. It forms when part of the Earth's **crust** collapses along a **fault** line. The African Rift Valley is the largest known. It stretches northwards from the Zambezi River in Africa to the Middle East.
There was a long line of lakes at the bottom of the rift valley.

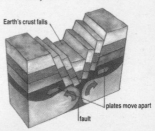

Earth's crust falls

plates move apart

fault

rime ► **hoar frost**

river ► page 122

river bed *noun*
A river bed is the base of the **channel** in which a **river** flows. It is made of rocks and mud and it may contain many kinds of water plants and animals.
The level of water was so low that we could walk along the river bed.

rock *noun*
Rock is the term used for hard **mineral** deposits. The Earth's **crust** is made of solid rocks about 70 kilometres deep. Rocks are named according to the way they were formed. The main types of rock are **igneous**, **metamorphic** and **sedimentary**. Small, individual rocks are called **stones**.
They had to drill the well through solid rock.

rock formation *noun*
A rock formation is the shape given to **rocks** by **wind**, **water** and heat. All over the world, wind and water have **eroded** rocks into unusual shapes. Cooling **igneous** rock produces quite different rock formations. Rock formations can be a major **feature** of the landscape.
There can be many different rock formations in a landscape.

ruby *noun*
A ruby is a precious stone which can be used as a **gem**. Rubies are a form of the mineral **corundum**. A ruby is red because it contains very small amounts of **chromium**. Many rubies come from mines in Burma.
Her ring had a bright red ruby at the centre.

runoff *noun*
Runoff is that part of the **rainfall** which reaches the **streams** and **rivers**. The rest either **evaporates** back into the **air** or seeps into **rocks** under the ground.
There was more runoff after the heavy rain.

S

saline *adjective*
Saline describes a liquid which contains **salt**. **Sea water** is a liquid which is saline, because it contains common salt.
He bathed his sore eye in a saline solution.

salinity *noun*
Salinity is a measure of the amount of any **salt** which is dissolved in water. All water, even fresh water, contains some salt. **Sea water** has a high salinity because it contains a large amount of salt. Some **lakes** have even higher levels of salinity than sea water.
We knew by the taste that the water had a high salinity.

salinization *noun*
Salinization is the process by which a **soil** contains more and more **salt**. **Evaporation** removes the water from the soil, leaving the salts behind. If there is too much salt in the soil, it becomes **infertile**, and crops will not grow. Salinization is common in the soil near the **coast** in warm regions and in the soil in dry regions.
The crops failed to grow in the soil because it had been affected by salinization.

salt *noun*
A salt is a kind of chemical **compound**. Salts are formed when an **acid** and a base react together. There are many different salts. Common salt, or sodium chloride, is the most widely known. Common salt makes the sea salty and can also be found underground as rock salt.
She added common salt to her food to bring out the flavour.

salt lake *noun*

A salt lake is a **lake** with a high **salinity**. Salt lakes form in hot, dry regions when water **evaporates** from the lake. This evaporation leaves the salts behind. The Dead Sea, in Israel, is a famous salt lake.
The water in the salt lake was so salty that she floated easily.

salt pan *noun*

A salt pan is a small **salt lake**. Common salt can be collected from salt pans. The water in a salt pan **evaporates** in the Sun and wind, and the salt is left behind as **crystals**.
They obtained large quantities of salt from the salt pans on the coast.

salt water *noun*

Salt water is **water** which contains a high level of dissolved **salts**. The **oceans** and seas and some inland **lakes** contain salt water.
They knew they were near the sea because the river contained salt water.

salt-marsh *noun*

A salt-marsh is an area of wet **ground** near the **coast** which is sometimes flooded by the sea. When the sea floods the ground, the water becomes salty.
The salt-marsh attracted many wild birds.

sand *noun*

Sand is a kind of **detritus**. It is made up of tiny grains of **minerals**, such as **quartz**. Sand is often found at the **coast**. Over many hundreds of years, the **waves** of the sea grind down the rocks into sand. Sand particles are smaller than two millimetres across.
The children used the damp sand to make models of buildings.

volcanic sand

quartz sand

sand from red sandstone

sand dune ▶ dune

sand-bank *noun*

A sand-bank is a mound of **sand** which is found in the **sea**, an **estuary** or a **river**. A sand-bank forms when a water **current** which is carrying sand slows down. The sand falls through the water and is deposited as a mound. Sand-banks can be a danger to boats as they can usually be seen only at low **tide**.
The ship ran aground on the sand-bank which was hidden below the water.

sea

sand-bank

sand-bar *noun*

A sand-bar is a narrow **sand-bank** at the mouth of a river or **estuary**.
They noticed several seals lying on the sand-bar.

sandstone *noun*

Sandstone is a kind of **sedimentary** rock or **stone**. It is made of sand grains held tightly together by **mud**. Sandstone is easy to cut and shape, and is often used for building. Sandstone is often a red colour.
The island was ringed by sandstone cliffs.

sandstorm *noun*

A sandstorm is a strong **wind** which carries grains of **sand**. In a sandstorm, sand and **dust** may be lifted to a great height and carried many kilometres. Sandstorms are common in sandy **deserts**.
They found it hard to see through the fierce sandstorm.

sapphire *noun*
A sapphire is a precious stone with a bright blue colour. Sapphire is almost as hard as **diamond**. Sapphire is a form of **corundum**.
A huge sapphire sparkled at the centre of the woman's necklace.

savanna *noun*
Savanna is a kind of dry, lowland **plain** found in the **tropics**. In a savanna, there are patches of **grassland** with scattered bushes and trees.
The lions moved across the open savanna in search of antelopes.

scale *noun*
Scale is a measure used to show the size of features shown on a **map**. The scale of a map compares the size of the details shown on the map with the actual size of the features.
A scale is also a set of regularly spaced marks, used for measuring. A thermometer has a scale marked in **degrees**, for measuring temperature. The **Beaufort Scale** measures the force of the wind.
We could see many details on the map because it had a large scale.

scarp ► **escarpment**

schist *noun*
Schist is a kind of **metamorphic** rock. In schist, the surface of the rock is very flaky and shiny. The mineral **mica** is a common type of schist.
The geologist showed us the shiny bands of schist in the rock face.

scree *noun*
Scree is a collection of loose **rocks** and **stones** on the side of a **mountain**. It is formed by the **weathering** of a rock face. Usually, the larger pieces of rock are at the base of the pile, with smaller stones higher up. Heaps of scree can often be seen at the foot of **cliffs** and steep **slopes** in mountainous country.
He walked very carefully over the scree in case he lost his footing on the loose rocks.

scrub *noun*
Scrub is the name for a dry habitat with many small bushes. Sometimes, scrub grows up after a **forest** has been cut down. Other types of scrub are found where there is not enough **rainfall** to allow trees to grow.
They travelled a long way through the scrub to reach the river.

sea *noun*
The sea is the great mass of **salt water** that covers more than three-quarters of the **Earth's** surface. Enormous areas of the sea are known as **oceans**.
The huge waves of the sea crashed against the rocks at the coast.

sea stack ► **needle**

sea water *noun*
Sea water is the water in the **sea**. Most sea water is very salty because of the **salts** that it contains. These include salts of **sodium**, **calcium** and **magnesium**.
At the mouth of the river, the fresh water mixed with sea water.

sea-bed *noun*
The sea-bed is the bottom of the **sea**. Like dry land, the sea-bed can be flat or can have huge **mountain** ranges and deep **valleys**.
The divers explored the sea-bed.

sea-floor spreading *noun*
Sea-floor spreading describes the movement of the Earth's **crust** at the **sea-bed**. Molten rock, or **lava**, comes to the surface at the **mid-oceanic ridges**. The rock is then pushed out sideways, making the sea-bed wider. The study of sea-floor spreading is part of **plate tectonics**.
The scientists measured the amount of sea-floor spreading on the sea-bed.

sea-level *noun*
Sea-level is the average height of the surface of the **sea**. The height of land is measured from sea-level.
The floods spread quickly because the land was below sea-level.

seam *noun*
A seam is a band of a **mineral** trapped between two layers of **rock**. **Coal** is often found in long seams.
The miners removed a large amount of coal by working straight along the seam.

seamount *noun*
A seamount is a single volcanic **mountain** rising up from the **sea-bed**. Although they are far below **sea-level**, seamounts can be over 3,500 metres high. Seamounts do not appear above the surface of the water.
The seamount rose up steeply from the flat, ocean floor.

sea-shore *noun*
The sea-shore is the land immediately next to the **sea**. Many sea-shores are covered with **sand**, but they may also be rocky or covered with **shingle**.
We searched the sea-shore for as many different kinds of rock as we could find.

season *noun*
A season is a part of the year which has a particular **climate**. In **temperate** regions, the four seasons are **spring**, **summer**, **autumn** and **winter**. These vary in both **temperature** and **rainfall**. In the **tropics**, there are usually two seasons. These are the hot, dry season and the hot, rainy season.
It was very wet because they arrived during the rainy season.

seaway *noun*
A seaway is a safe way over the ocean which has been drawn on a **chart** for ships to follow. It is also a very wide, deep canal.
The seaway took us safely past the islands.

sediment *noun*
Sediment is the solid that settles at the bottom of a liquid. **Stones** and **mud** gather as sediment at the bottom of **rivers**, **streams** and on the **sea-bed**.
The bed of the lake was covered in sediment.

sedimentary *adjective*
Sedimentary describes a type of **rock** or **stone**. Sedimentary rocks are those which are formed from **sediments**. Some kinds, such as **breccia**, are formed from small pieces of other types of rock. Other kinds, such as **chalk**, are made up of the **shells** of tiny animals.
The quarry contained sedimentary rock.

sedimentology *noun*
Sedimentology is the study of **sedimentary** rocks. Sedimentology helps in the exploration for **oil**, **natural gas** and **coal**.
Her knowledge of sedimentology helped the geologist discover a source of coal.

seismic wave *noun*

A seismic wave is a wave of **energy** which travels through the **Earth** from an **earthquake**. Seismic waves spread out from the **focus** of an earthquake and can cause much damage. They are felt as **foreshocks**, **aftershocks**, or **tremors** on the land. At sea, a seismic wave may produce a **tsunami**.
The scientists switched on their instruments to record the strength of the seismic waves.

seismograph *noun*

A seismograph is an instrument which measures how much the **ground** shakes or vibrates. A pen records **seismic waves** on paper fixed to a moving drum. It can also record movements caused by explosions.
The geologist recorded the distant earthquake on a seismograph.

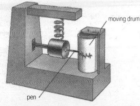

seismology *noun*

Seismology is the study of **seismic waves**. It gives us information about **earthquakes**, the structure of the **Earth** and about what happens inside the Earth.
She studied seismology to learn about the Earth's crust.

serpentine *noun*

Serpentine is a **mineral**. It is found in **igneous** rocks. Serpentine is normally dark green, but it can also be brown, yellow or white. Serpentine can be carved and polished to make ornaments.
On the desk, there was a dark, shiny paperweight made of serpentine.

settlement *noun*

A settlement is formed when a group of people set up, or establish, a new village or town. A settlement is also any collection of dwellings. Some settlements are as large as a city, such as Mexico City. Other settlements are as small as a few huts in the jungle.
The fishermen built a settlement by the sea.

sextant *noun*

A sextant is a measuring instrument. It measures the angle of the Sun, the Moon or the stars from the horizon. Sailors at sea can work out their **latitude** with a sextant.
The sextant helped the ship's captain calculate the position of the nearest island.

shaft *noun*

A shaft is a straight tunnel going into the ground. Many **mines** are made by digging shafts.
The miners went down the shaft in a lift.

shale *noun*

Shale is a kind of **sedimentary** rock. It is brittle and breaks easily. Shale is formed when **clay** and **silt** deposits turn to rock.
The cliffs were too dangerous to climb because they were formed from shale.

shell *noun*
A shell is the hard, outer covering of some animals. Shells are made mostly of **calcium**. Some kinds of **limestone**, such as **chalk**, are made of tiny shells which have been crushed and packed tightly together.
He found many cowrie shells on the beach.

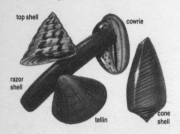

top shell

cowrie

razor shell

tellin

cone shell

shield *noun*
A shield is part of the Earth's **crust**. It is a large area of old **metamorphic** and **igneous** rocks of **Precambrian** age. These rocks are flat because they have not been folded or buckled into **mountains**.
The rocks of the Canadian shield are some of the oldest rocks in the world.

shingle *noun*
Shingle is **pebbles** or coarse **gravel** found on **beaches**. The stones in shingle are between about one and seven centimetres across. They are smooth because they have been **eroded** by the **waves**.
Over millions of years, the action of the waves will turn the shingle into sand.

shoal *noun*
A shoal is a bank of **sand** or **mud** in a **river** or in the sea. Shoals form when slow-flowing river water deposits the **sediment** it has been carrying.
The digging machines removed the shoals from along the river channel to allow the water to flow.

shock wave *noun*
A shock wave is a sudden **wave** of enormous pressure. Like sound waves, shock waves can travel through air, water or the ground. Most shock waves are caused by **earthquakes**. Explosions and **thunder** can also cause shock waves.
The distant explosion caused a shock wave.

sial *noun*
Sial is the material which forms the **continental crust**. The sial lies underneath the continents. It is made mainly of **granite** and contains **silica** and **aluminium**.
The rocks of the continental crust are largely made up of sial.

sierra *noun*
A sierra is a **mountain chain** containing a number of **peaks**. A famous example of a sierra is the Sierra Nevada in Spain.
The mules carried the luggage slowly along the path that led over the sierra.

silica *noun*
Silica is the main **chemical** in the Earth's **crust**. It is made of **silicon** and **oxygen**. **Quartz**, **flint**, **opal** and **sinter** are all forms of silica. Silica is used in making glass and cement.
The silica used in the glass factory was ground to a fine powder.

silicates *noun*
Silicates are the most common **minerals**. Silicates are compounds containing **silicon** and **oxygen**, with one or more extra **element**.
The geologist explained that many of the Earth's rocks and minerals are silicates.

silicon *noun*
Silicon is an **element**. It is very common in the Earth's **crust**. Most silicon is combined with **oxygen**, as **silica**. Brick, **cement** and glass all contain silicon. Pure silicon is used in computers and other electrical devices.
Silicon is the second most common element after oxygen.

sill *noun*

A sill is a layer of **igneous** rock trapped inside another type of rock, such as **metamorphic** rock. A sill forms when **magma** flows inside the metamorphic rock and then becomes solid. A sill is often harder than the rock around it.

The sill of hard rock stuck out from the side of the cliff.

silt *noun*

Silt is a dust-like substance made up of tiny particles of **rock**. **Rivers** and **streams** carry silt, which settles on the river bed as **sediment**. Silt can build up in **reservoirs**.

The sunken boat was partly covered in silt.

Silurian *adjective*

Silurian describes a **period** in **geological time**. The Silurian Period lasted from about 438 million years ago to about 408 million years ago.

The first land plants appeared during the Silurian Period

silver *noun*

Silver is an **element**. It is a white, shiny **metal**. Silver is commonly found as an ore together with **lead**, **zinc** or **copper**. Silver is sometimes found in its pure form. It is used to make ornaments and to conduct electricity. Silver **compounds** are used to make films for photography.

The photographic film in her camera contained silver.

sima *noun*

Sima is the material which forms the **oceanic crust**. The sima layer lies underneath the oceans. The sima layer also lies under the **sial** of the **continental crust**. It is made mainly of **basalt** and contains **silica** and **magnesium**.

The rocks of the sea-bed are made of sima.

sink-hole *noun*

A sink-hole is a steep-sided hole in the surface of the ground. Sink-holes are common in **limestone** areas, such as in **karst** landscapes. Water from streams and rivers may fall through sink-holes into a **cave** below.

The sink-hole led to a series of deep caves.

sinter *noun*

Sinter is a **deposit** which is made of **silicates**. It is found around the edges of hot **springs** or **geysers**.

The sinter formed hard banks and ledges around the mouth of the geyser.

sirocco *noun*

The sirocco is a kind of **wind**. It is a warm, dry wind which blows northwards from the Sahara towards the Mediterranean region.

We arrived in Italy as the sirocco began to blow.

slate *noun*

Slate is a kind of **metamorphic** rock or **stone**. It is formed from **shale** or **mudstone**. Slate has a smooth surface and it splits easily in flat slabs. Slate is used for building and for roofing tiles.

When the gale blew, several pieces of slate fell from the roof.

sleet *noun*
Sleet is a mixture of **rain** and **snow**. Sleet can also be snow or **hail** which has half melted and then falls from the sky.
They went out in the sleet and got very cold and wet.

slope *noun*
A slope is a piece of ground which rises or falls. On a **hill** or **mountain**, the slope is usually steepest near the top and becomes more gentle towards the bottom.
The walker looked for the path up the slope of the hill.

small-scale *adjective*
Small-scale is a term which describes a kind of **map**. A small-scale map covers a large area, but does not show much detail.
The small-scale map of the mountains showed the peaks but not the roads.

smog *noun*
Smog is a kind of **fog**. It is a mixture of fog and smoke and other forms of pollution. Smog occurs in cities where fog is common and where there is much smoke in the air.
The thick smog settled over the city like a huge blanket.

snow *noun*
Snow is water which falls from **clouds** as **crystals** of **ice**. Snow forms when water **vapour** in the clouds turns directly into ice, without first becoming liquid.
The snow fell thickly and lay on the cold ground for weeks.

snowflakes

snow line *noun*
The snow line is the level on a **hill** or **mountain** above which the **snow** never melts. The height of the snow line varies with **latitude** and climate. It also depends upon the direction of the **wind** and the steepness of the slope.
The wolves came down below the snow line to hunt for food.

snowfield *noun*
A snowfield is a wide expanse of permanent **snow**. Snowfields are found in high mountains and around the **North Pole** and **South Pole**. Some snowfields may turn to ice and form **glaciers**.
The snowfield formed in a hollow in the rocks.

soapstone *noun*
Soapstone is a **mineral**. It is a smooth stone which feels soapy. Soapstone is a grey-green or brown form of **talc**. It can be carved easily and is used to make ornaments.
He carved the tiny figure from soapstone.

sodium *noun*
Sodium is an **element**. It is a **metal** which forms many important **compounds**, including common **salt** and soda. Many **minerals** contain sodium.
The pure sodium fizzed fiercely in the water.

soft water *noun*
Soft water is **water** which does not contain **magnesium** or **calcium** salts. Soap in soft water lathers quickly and does not form scum. The opposite of soft water is **hard water**.
He needed only a small amount of soap powder to wash his clothes in the soft water.

soil *noun*

Soil is the layers of **earth** which lie on top of solid **rock**. Soil is a mixture of small pieces of rock, **minerals** and **humus**. Most plants need soil in order to grow.

The farmers planted their crops in the soil.

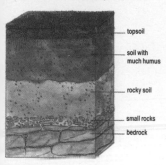

- topsoil
- soil with much humus
- rocky soil
- small rocks
- bedrock

soil erosion *noun*

Soil erosion is the loss of **soil** from the surface of the ground. When the **wind** blows, dry soil may be blown away. Water can also cause soil erosion when heavy **rainfall** washes the soil away.

The farmers could no longer plant their crops because of the soil erosion.

solar *adjective*

Solar is a word which describes anything to do with the **Sun**. The Sun is part of our solar system. Solar heat is heat which comes from the Sun.

The solar wind travels from the Sun at a speed of about one and a half million kilometres an hour.

solar energy *noun*

Solar energy is energy which comes directly from the **Sun**. Solar energy can be used to make electricity and to heat water.

The house was heated using solar energy.

solstice *noun*

The solstice is the day in the year when the Sun reaches a position furthest north or south of the **Equator**. The Sun reaches its furthest north over the **Tropic of Cancer** on June 21st. It reaches its furthest south over the **Tropic of Capricorn** on December 21st. The position of the Sun seems to move from one side of the Equator to the other because of the rotation of the Earth on its **axis**.

The two solstices are called winter and summer solstices, depending on whether the days are getting shorter or longer.

sonar *noun*

Sonar is a system which uses sound waves to measure the depth of water. An instrument sends out pulses of sound, which bounce back off the **sea-bed**. The depth of water is measured on a depth scale. Shoals of fish can also be detected using sonar. Some forms of sonar are called **echo sounders**.

The scientists measured the depth of water in the channel using sonar.

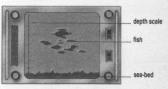

- depth scale
- fish
- sea-bed

sound *noun*

A sound is a narrow **channel** of the **sea**. A sound usually runs between the mainland and an **offshore** island.

They watched the ships racing each other up the sound.

source *noun*

A source is the place where a **river** or **stream** begins to flow. A river runs from its source, which is often a **spring**, right down to its **mouth** at an **estuary** or a **delta**.

She followed the river to its source high up in the mountains.

South Pole *noun*
The South Pole is the point furthest south on
the **Earth**. It lies close to the centre of the
continent of **Antarctica**. There are two south
poles. These are the geographical South Pole
and the **magnetic pole**.
*The Norwegian explorer Raold Amundsen
reached the South Pole first, in 1911.*

southern hemisphere *noun*
The southern hemisphere is the part of the
Earth which lies south of the **Equator**. The
continents of Australia and most of South
America lie in the southern hemisphere.
*The ship crossed over the Equator and sailed
into the waters of the southern hemisphere.*

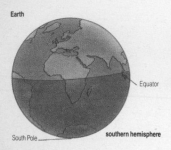

speleology *noun*
Speleology is the study and exploration of
caves. It includes the **geology** of caves, and
the study of the animals and plants which live
in caves.
*He studied speleology to find out why bats
make their homes in caves.*

spit *noun*
A spit is a long, narrow stretch of **sand** or
gravel running out into the **sea**. Spits form
when water **currents** running along the
sea-shore deposit sand and gravel. A spit
often encloses an **estuary** or a **bay**.
The spit separated the sea from the river.

spring *noun*
A spring is the place where a **stream** or **river**
rises out of the **ground**. Springs form above
impermeable rock which lies at the surface
of sloping ground.
The spring was the source of a large river.

spring tide *noun*
A spring tide is a **tide** with a large difference
in water level between high tide and low tide.
Spring tides occur when the **gravities** of the
Sun and the Moon pull in the same direction.
They happen twice in every month. The
opposite of a spring tide is a **neap tide**.
The spring tide flooded the road.

squall *noun*
A squall is a kind of **wind**. A squall is sudden,
short and rather violent. Squalls are common
during **storms**.
They ran for shelter to avoid the strong squall.

St Elmo's fire *noun*
St Elmo's fire is a kind of **lightning**. It is a
blue-green glow seen in the air during
storms. It can sometimes be seen on the
masts of ships at sea.
*The sailors saw the St Elmo's fire lighting up
the clouds nearby.*

stalactite *noun*
A stalactite is a pointed piece of **limestone**
hanging down from the roof of a **cave**. It has
a shape like an **icicle**. Stalactites are made
of calcium carbonate. **Hard water** drips down
and **evaporates**, leaving the calcium
carbonate behind to form a stalactite.
The opposite of a stalactite is a **stalagmite**.
They looked up at the stalactites.

134

stalagmite *noun*
A stalagmite is a mound or spike of **limestone** rising up from the floor of a **cave**. **Hard water** falls onto the spike and **evaporates**, leaving calcium carbonate. The opposite of a stalagmite is a **stalactite**.
The stalagmite looked like a giant candle.

steppe *noun*
A steppe is a dry, grassy **plain** without trees which is found in central Europe and Siberia. Steppes are found in **climates** which are too dry for trees to grow. Steppe **soils** are deep and fertile. In North America, these grassy plains are called **prairies**.
The farmers grew wheat on the fertile steppe.

stone ▶ page 136

storm *noun*
A storm is a strong **wind**. A storm measures force 10 or 11 on the **Beaufort Scale**. Some storms bring heavy **rain** and **thunder**.
The storm caused very bad flooding.

strait *noun*
A strait is a narrow strip of **sea**. A strait connects two seas or **oceans**. The Strait of Gibraltar connects the Atlantic Ocean with the Mediterranean Sea.
The boats followed each other in a line through the strait.

Spain
Gibraltar
Strait of Gibraltar
Mediterranean Sea
Morocco

stratigraphy *noun*
Stratigraphy is the study of the different kinds of **layer**, or **stratum**, of **rocks**. In stratigraphy, a **geologist** can study the different rocks or **fossils** to work out when the rocks and fossils were formed.
The geologist used stratigraphy to find out the age of the rocks.

stratocumulus *adjective*
Stratocumulus describes a kind of **cloud**. These clouds form at a low level in the sky and are grey and white. They form as a **warm front** passes. Stratocumulus clouds are rounded in shape. They often produce tiny drops of rain which fall as drizzle.
We expected rain when we saw the stratocumulus clouds approaching.

stratopause *noun*
The stratopause is part of the Earth's **atmosphere**. It is the upper edge of the **stratosphere**, and lies at a height of about 50 kilometres above the surface of the Earth.
The temperature of the stratopause is about 0 degrees Celsius.

stratosphere *noun*
The stratosphere is part of the Earth's **atmosphere**. It lies above the **tropopause**, and it is about 40 kilometres thick. There are very few **clouds** in the stratosphere. This layer contains most of the **ozone** found in the atmosphere. The ozone layer forms a protective shield. This stops harmful **radiation** reaching the Earth from the Sun.
The rocket passed quickly through the stratosphere.

stratum (plural **strata**) *noun*
A stratum is a **layer** in **sedimentary** rock. Strata vary in thickness from less than a centimetre to many metres. They are normally horizontal. The word stratum is also used to describe a layer of the Earth's **atmosphere**, such as the **ionosphere**.
We could see the bands of different strata on the cliff face.

135

stone *noun*

A stone is a hard, **mineral** deposit. It is a
small piece of **rock**. Stones are formed from
the three main types of rock. These are
igneous, **metamorphic** and **sedimentary**
rock.
*The three major ways in which stones can be
made are shown below.*

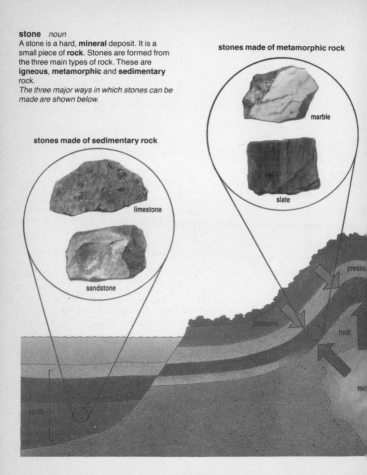

stones made of metamorphic rock

marble

slate

stones made of sedimentary rock

limestone

sandstone

pressu

pressure

heat

strata

ma

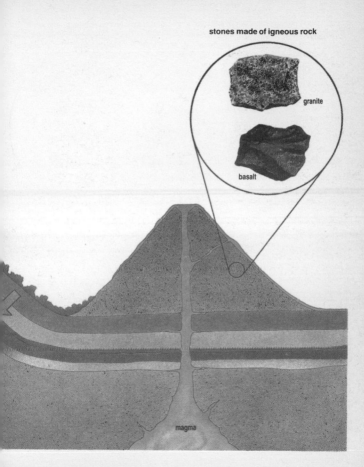

stones made of igneous rock

granite

basalt

magma

stratus *adjective*
Stratus describes a kind of **cloud**. Stratus
clouds form low in the sky. They are light grey
with flat bases. They form when warm and
cold air mix together. Stratus clouds usually
bring a fine, long-lasting rain.
*It started to rain when the stratus clouds
covered the whole sky.*

streak colour *noun*
The streak colour is a feature of **minerals**.
If a piece of a mineral is rubbed on a rough
white surface, it will leave a coloured mark.
The mark may not be the same colour as the
mineral. Each mineral has its own streak
colour. **Geologists** use these streak colours
to help them to identify minerals.
*We saw the mineral's characteristic streak
colour on the broken surface of the rock.*

streak colour

hematite

stream *noun*
A stream is a small **channel** of **water** which
flows continually. Streams start at a **spring** or
lake and join together to form **rivers**. Stream
can also be used to describe a current or a
continuous flow of a liquid or a gas, such as
molten rock or air.
The stream flowed swiftly through the fields.

stress *noun*
Stress is strong pressure in the **rocks** or **soil**
of the **Earth**. Stress is caused by movements
in the Earth's **crust** which push rocks against
each other. Stress causes rocks to bend and
creates **faults** and **folds**. High levels of stress
can also cause **earthquakes**.
*The layers of rock had been bent by the stress
in the ground below.*

stria (plural **striae**) *noun*
A stria is a tiny groove or scratch on the
surface of a **rock**. A stria is caused by ice,
often during a **glaciation**. **Stones** and rocks
in the ice at the bottom of a **glacier** scratch
the rock below, leaving striae on the rock
surface. Another word for stria is striation.
*The geologist could tell which way the ice had
moved by looking at each stria on the rocks.*

sub- *prefix*
Sub- is a prefix that describes something
under, below or less.
The subsoil was dry and infertile.

subduction zone *noun*
A subduction zone is an area on the Earth's
crust where a **tectonic plate** goes down into
the **mantle**. Subduction zones lie below
oceanic **trenches**.
*The Earth's crust gradually disappeared along
the subduction zone.*

submarine *adjective*
Submarine describes an object or habitat
which is found below the surface of the **sea**.
*The aquarium contained a selection of
submarine life.*

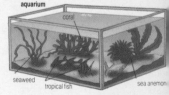
aquarium
coral
seaweed
tropical fish
sea anemone

submarine plain ▶ abyssal plain

submersible vehicle *noun*
A submersible vehicle is one which can move
about under water. A **bathyscaph** is one kind
of submersible vehicle.
*They travelled in a submersible vehicle to look
at the sea-bed.*

138

subsidence *noun*
Subsidence is a sinking of **earth** or **soil**. It can be caused by **rocks** and soils collapsing into a space below the ground. Caves and mines can collapse and cause subsidence.
The house could not be built over the old mine for fear of subsidence.

subsoil *noun*
Subsoil is the **soil** below the surface soil, or **topsoil**. The subsoil is less often disturbed than the topsoil and contains less **organic** material. The subsoil also has more **clay** and **minerals** than the topsoil. The subsoil lies above the **bedrock**.
The deep plough made a furrow right down to the subsoil.

subterranean *adjective*
Subterranean describes something that is below the **ground**. A subterranean **river** is a river which flows under the ground.
The path led down into a series of subterranean caves.

sub-tropical *adjective*
Sub-tropical describes two regions that lie near the **tropics**. One sub-tropical region reaches north from the **Tropic of Cancer** to **latitude** 40 degrees north, and the other sub-tropical region reaches south from the **Tropic of Capricorn** to latitude 40 degrees south.
Crops grew well in the sub-tropical climate.

sulphur *noun*
Sulphur is an **element**. It is greenish-yellow in its pure form, and it is often found as **compounds**. With **oxygen**, it forms the poisonous **gas** called **sulphur dioxide**. Sulphur is used to make many things, including matches and medicines.
The volcano smelt strongly of sulphur long after it had erupted.

sulphur dioxide *noun*
Sulphur dioxide is a poisonous **gas**. It is made when **chemicals** containing **sulphur** are burned. Smoke from chimneys often contains sulphur dioxide. It is one of the causes of **acid rain**.
We could smell the sulphur dioxide in the smoke from the factory.

summer *noun*
Summer is the name for the warmest **season** of the year in **temperate** climates. In the summer, the **Sun** is at its highest point in the sky and the days are longest. In the **northern hemisphere**, summer lasts from May to August. In the **southern hemisphere**, summer lasts from November to February.
By the time it was summer, the snow on the mountains had melted.

summit *noun*
Summit is the highest point of a **hill** or **mountain**. The summit of Mount Everest, the **Earth's** highest mountain, lies at 8,848 metres above **sea-level**.
We climbed quickly to the summit.

Sun *noun*
The Sun is a star. Scientists think that it has a liquid centre, surrounded by a large mass of very hot **gas**. In **orbit** around the Sun is a **solar system** of nine planets. Our world, **Earth**, is the third planet from the Sun. Radiation from the Sun reaches Earth as heat and **sunlight**. This **solar energy** allows life to exist on our world.
The Earth makes a complete orbit of the Sun once a year.

sunlight *noun*
Sunlight is the light which reaches the **Earth** from the **Sun**. All life on Earth depends upon sunlight. Plants need sunlight to make their food and grow. Animals feed on the plants, or on other animals. Sunlight is a form of **radiation**.
One side of the valley was in bright sunlight while the other side was in shadow.

super-continent *noun*
A super-continent describes one of the huge **continents** which may have existed very early in the history of the **Earth**. Some scientists think that the continents of today were once joined together in a single super-continent, called **Pangaea**.
Scientist think that the super-continents of the past were much larger than the continents of today.

surf *noun*
Surf is the foam and spray caused by **waves** as they break on the **sea-shore**, or on rocks. Animals and plants living in the surf are firmly fixed to the rocks, or live in burrows beneath the surface of the ground, so that they are not swept away.
The large waves made a great amount of surf as they broke upon the sea-shore.

surface *noun*
The surface is the outer layer of a substance, such as a **rock** or **mineral**. Many rocks have rough surfaces. **Crystals** have smooth surfaces. The surface of a broken **flint** is also very smooth.
The surface of the rock was covered in bumps and ridges.

survey *noun*
A survey is a careful investigation of an area or **region**. A survey can look for particular **features** or substances. A geological survey tries to discover the main **rock** types and **soils** of an area.
The survey revealed that the rocks might contain gold.

swamp *noun*
A swamp is a kind of **wetland**. In a swamp, the water level is high and the plants growing in it are always surrounded by water.
The swamp contained an unusual variety of animals and plants.

mangrove swamp

swell *noun*
Swell is the movement of the open **sea**. The swell of the sea is caused by long, rolling **waves** which do not break at the surface. Swell causes boats and ships to sway and roll in the water.
As soon as the ferry left the harbour, we felt the swell of the sea.

syncline *noun*
A syncline is a kind of fold in **sedimentary** and **metamorphic** rocks. In a syncline, layers, or **strata**, of rock fold downwards in a **basin**, with the younger rocks at the top. A syncline is the opposite of an **anticline**.
The geologist pointed out where the rocks dipped down in a syncline.

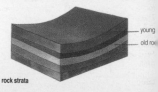
young
old roc
rock strata

140

T

tableland *noun*
A tableland is a **landscape** with a large area
of flat, high land. The surface of the land is
flat, like a table.
*We could see the outline of the tableland in
the distance.*

taiga *noun*
Taiga is the **forest** which lies just to the south
of the **Arctic** region. The taiga contains
coniferous and evergreen trees, such as
spruce and pine. It stretches for many
thousands of kilometres, mostly in Siberia.
*It was difficult to follow the deer in the dark
forests of the taiga.*

talc *noun*
Talc is a soft **mineral**. Its colour is white to
pale green. Talc is found in **metamorphic**
rocks, and contains **magnesium** and **silicon**.
There are large **deposits** of talc in India and
in Austria. When it is ground up, it is called
talcum powder. The solid form of talc is also
called **soapstone**.
*He ground up the talc until it turned into a
white powder.*

talus ▶ scree

tectonic plate ▶ page 142

temperate *adjective*
Temperate describes a region or **climate**
which is neither very hot nor very cold. The
temperate zones lie between the **tropics** and
the **polar** regions.
*A temperate climate is warmer than a polar
climate.*

temperature *noun*
Temperature is a kind of measurement.
It measures how hot or cold something
is. Temperature is measured in **degrees**
using a **thermometer**.
*They had to move into the shade because
the temperature was so high.*

terminal moraine ▶ moraine

terrain *noun*
Terrain is the surface of an area of country.
In a flat terrain, the surface is level, but in
hilly terrain it is very bumpy.
We crossed rough, rocky terrain.

terrestrial *adjective*
Terrestrial describes something that lives on
the **land**. Most animals and plants are
terrestrial, and feed and grow on dry land.
*At the edge of the lake, the aquatic plants
gave way to terrestrial plants.*

Tertiary *adjective*
Tertiary describes a sub-era in **geological
time**. The Tertiary sub-era lasted from
about 65 million to about 2 million
years ago.
*The mountains of the Himalayas were formed
during the Tertiary sub-era.*

Tethys Sea *noun*
The Tethys Sea is the name given to the sea
which once lay between **Laurasia** and
Gondwanaland. Scientists think the sea was
formed about 250 million years ago when
Pangaea split into two parts.
*The map showed where scientists thought the
Tethys Sea once lay.*

tectonic plate *noun*

A tectonic plate is a section of the Earth's **crust** which moves as a single piece. There are seven major tectonic plates on the surface of the Earth and several smaller ones. Where two or more moving plates meet, the surface of the Earth may bend or crack and **earthquakes** or **volcanoes** may occur. *The rocks had folded and buckled where the tectonic plates met.*

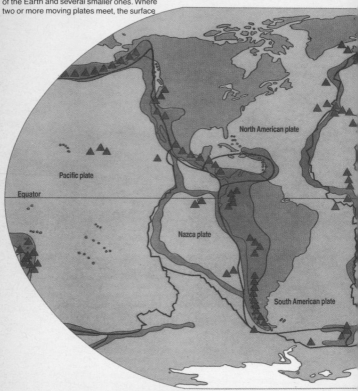

North American plate

Pacific plate

Equator

Nazca plate

South American plate

map of distribution of volcanoes and earthquakes

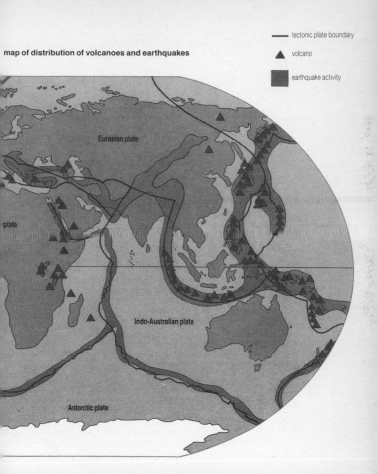

texture *noun*

Texture is a word that describes the size
and shape of particles in **rock** or **soil**. It also
describes the way the particles are arranged.
Some rocks, such as quartzite, can have a
fine, smooth texture. Others, like **granite**,
are coarse.
*The tiny rock particles gave the soil a very
rough texture.*

granite   quartzite

thaw *verb*

Thaw describes the melting of a substance
which has been frozen. Snow or ice thaw
when the **temperature** rises above freezing,
or 0 degrees Celsius.
*When the Sun came out, the ice thawed and
turned into water.*

theodolite *noun*

A theodolite is an instrument used in
a **survey**. A theodolite measures the angles
between two points. It is a small telescope
which is connected to a vertical and
a horizontal **scale**. A theodolite is usually
mounted on a tripod.
*The surveyor used the theodolite to measure
the angle between the hill and the river.*

telescope

scales

tripod

thermal *noun*

A thermal is a rising column of warm **air**.
Thermals form over hot ground when
convection currents develop in the air. Many
birds soar upwards on thermals to help them
gain height.
*The glider circled slowly upwards, using the
thermals to rise in the air.*

thermocline *noun*

The thermocline is found in the **sea** and in
large **lakes**. The thermocline is the layer of
water between the warm water at the surface
and the cold, deeper water. The water at the
top of the thermocline is warmer than the
water at the bottom. The thermocline in the
sea lies at a depth of about 100 to 200 metres.
*The divers swam down to the cooler waters of
the thermocline.*

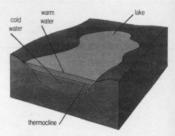

warm
water   lake

cold
water

thermocline

thermometer *noun*

A thermometer is an instrument for measuring
temperature. Some thermometers have a
column of liquid, such as **mercury**, in a tube.
This liquid expands as it warms and moves up
the tube. A **scale** next to the tube indicates
the temperature in **degrees**. Some
thermometers have a digital display which
shows the temperature in numbers.
*She measured the temperature of the air with
the thermometer on the outside wall of her
house.*

thunder *noun*

Thunder is the sound made during a **thunderstorm** when electricity is released from **clouds**. Thunder usually makes a deep, rumbling noise. It is caused when **lightning** heats the air very quickly. We see lightning before we hear thunder because sound travels more slowly than light.
The sudden thunder frightened the animals.

thunderstorm *noun*

A thunderstorm is a **storm** which is accompanied by **thunder** and flashes of **lightning**. Thunderstorms happen when strong **convection currents** develop in the air. They can also occur when a **cold front** passes. Thunderstorms are common throughout the year in the **tropics**, but are almost unknown in **polar** regions.
The thunderstorm brought thunder, lightning and heavy rain.

tidal *adjective*

Tidal describes something which is affected by the **tide** or which is caused by the **ebb** and **flow** of the tides.
The tidal waters of the sea turned the river water salty.

tidal wave *noun*

A tidal wave is a large **wave** usually caused by the movement of the **tides**. Tidal waves called **tsunamis** can also be caused by the **shock waves** that follow an **earthquake** or volcanic **eruption**. Tidal waves can cause a great deal of damage when they flood the land close to the coast.
They built a barrier to protect the farmland from tidal waves.

tide ▶ page 146

tiger's eye *noun*

Tiger's eye is a **mineral**. It is a bright, yellow-brown form of **quartz**. Tiger's eyes are used in jewellery as semi-precious stones.
His ring contained a large tiger's eye.

time zone *noun*

A time zone is a region of the **Earth** where the time is the same. The Earth has 24 time zones. Each time zone is 15 degrees of **longitude** apart and is usually bounded by **meridians**. In each time zone, the time is a complete number of hours ahead of or behind the time at the **Greenwich meridian**.
We had to re-set our watches as we crossed over into the new time zone.

tin *noun*

Tin is an **element**. It is a white **metal**. The most common tin **ore** is **cassiterite**. Tin may be used to coat other metals. Cans for food are often made with tin. Tin is also used to make **alloy**.
Malaysia is the world's greatest producer of tin.

titanium *noun*

Titanium is an **element**. It is a white **metal** which is found mainly as a compound with **oxygen**. Titanium is used for making **alloys**, especially for building aircraft. Titanium **oxide** is used as a white colour in paint.
The metal in the aircraft's wing was an alloy of titanium.

topaz *noun*

Topaz is a **mineral**. It may have yellow, blue or colourless **crystals**. Topaz contains **aluminium** and **silica**. It is found mainly in **igneous** rocks. Topaz is a semi-precious stone which is used in jewellery.
The bracelet had a string of stones of bright yellow topaz.

tide *noun*

A tide is the regular movement of **sea water** towards and away from the land. Tides are caused by the **gravities** of the Moon and Sun, which pull the sea away from the Earth. Tides with the smallest difference between high and low tides are called **neap tides**. Tides with the biggest difference between high and low tides are called **spring tides**.
The ship sailed away at high tide.

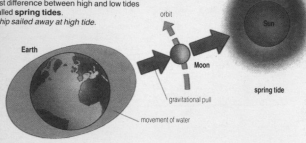

Earth

orbit

Moon

Sun

gravitational pull

movement of water

spring tide

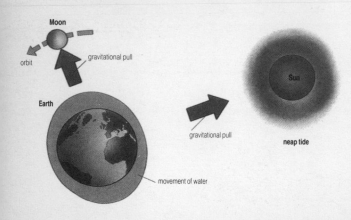

Moon

orbit

gravitational pull

Earth

Sun

gravitational pull

movement of water

neap tide

topographic map *noun*

A topographic map shows all the **features** of a **landscape**. It includes natural features, such as hills, valleys and rivers. It also includes objects that have been made, such as roads, bridges and towns. The map uses **contour** lines and the heights of **summits** to show the **topography** of the landscape.
We used a topographic map to plan our walk over the hills.

topography *noun*

Topography describes all the surface **features** of a **landscape**. These features include the hills and slopes of the land, the **soils** and vegetation, and things that have been made by people.
The topography of the area was dominated by rugged mountains.

topsoil *noun*

Topsoil is the surface layer of the **ground**. It is usually made up of loose **soil**. The topsoil contains large amounts of **humus**. Plants are rooted in the topsoil and take their water and minerals from it.
The water from the flood removed most of the topsoil from the hillside.

tor *noun*

A tor is a small area of **rock** which is exposed at the top of a rounded hill. Tors appear when the surrounding rocks have been worn away by **erosion**. Some tors at the top of hills have become landmarks.
We could see the tor outlined against the sky at the top of the hill.

tornado *noun*

A tornado is a kind of **wind**. In a tornado, the wind moves very quickly in a circular pattern around an area of very low **atmospheric pressure**. Tornadoes only last for about one or two hours, but they can be very destructive. They are common in the Great Plains region of North America. Other names for a tornado are a twister and a whirlwind.
The tornado left a track of flattened corn across the field.

swirling winds

tourmaline *noun*

Tourmaline is a **mineral**. The hard **crystals** of tourmaline are used as semi-precious stones. Tourmaline can have many colours, including black, blue or red. Tourmaline contains **sodium**, **calcium**, **boron**, **silica** and metals such as **aluminium**. It is found in **igneous** and **metamorphic** rocks.
He chose a ring with a dark red tourmaline.

trace element *noun*

A trace element is an **element** which plants and animals need for healthy growth. Only small amounts of trace elements are required. **Manganese**, **boron** and **cobalt** are examples of trace elements.
The rich soil had a good supply of all the trace elements the plant needed.

trade winds *noun*
Trade winds are steady **winds** which blow
from the east towards the **Equator**. In the
northern hemisphere, the trade winds blow
from the **Tropic of Cancer** to the Equator.
In the **southern hemisphere**, they blow
from the **Tropic of Capricorn** to the Equator.
Trade winds are strongest over the sea.
*The yacht picked up speed when it reached
the trade winds.*

tree *noun*
A tree is a large, woody plant with a tall trunk.
Some trees are evergreen and keep their
leaves all year round. Others are deciduous
and lose their leaves every year. The largest
trees live for hundreds of years and may
reach heights of over 100 metres.
Many trees grow in forests.

tree line *noun*
The tree line is the limit on a **mountain**, and
towards the **poles**, beyond which trees
cannot grow. Beyond the tree line it is too cold
for trees to survive.
*We walked to the tree line and then climbed to
the summit of the mountain.*

tremor *noun*
A tremor is a **shock wave** which travels
through the Earth's **crust**. The tremors
caused by **earthquakes** can be felt over a
long distance. Large, underground explosions
may also cause tremors.
*The scientists recorded the tremors from the
earthquake to find out how powerful it was.*

trench *noun*
A trench is a long, deep **valley** on the **ocean
floor**. The deepest trench is the Mariana
Trench in the western Pacific Ocean. This
reaches a depth of more than 11,000 metres.
Trenches have steep sides and are often
found by **subduction zones** at the edge
of **tectonic plates**.
The sea-bed fell steeply into the trench.

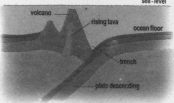

Triassic *adjective*
Triassic describes a **period** in **geological
time**. The Triassic Period lasted from about
248 million years ago to about 213 million
years ago. The Triassic Period is the earliest
part of the **Mesozoic** Era.
*The first dinosaurs appeared during the
Triassic Period.*

tributary *noun*
A tributary is a small **river** or **stream** which
flows into a larger one. Most rivers are joined
by many tributaries as they flow from their
source down towards the sea.
*We sailed down the tributary until it joined the
main river.*

trilobite *noun*
A trilobite is a kind of **fossil**. Trilobites lived in
the sea from the **Cambrian** Period until the
Permian Period. The largest trilobites were
about one metre long and the smallest about
one centimetre long.
The rocks contained fossils of trilobites.

Tropic of Cancer *noun*
The Tropic of Cancer is an imaginary line
around the **Earth** to the north of the **Equator**.
It lies at 23½ degrees **latitude** north. The
Tropic of Cancer marks the northern limit
of the **tropics**.
*The Tropic of Cancer runs through the middle
of the Sahara.*

Tropic of Capricorn *noun*
The Tropic of Capricorn is an imaginary line
around the **Earth** to the south of the **Equator**.
It lies at 23½ degrees **latitude** south. The
Tropic of Capricorn marks the southern limit
of the **tropics**.
*The city of São Paulo in Brazil lies close to the
Tropic of Capricorn.*

tropical *adjective*
Tropical describes something found in the
tropics. A tropical **climate** is one with no cool
season. It often has a heavy **rainfall** as well.
The monkeys lived in a tropical climate.

tropics *noun*
The tropics is an area with a **tropical** climate.
It lies between the **Tropic of Cancer** and the
Tropic of Capricorn. In the tropics, the
temperatures are high throughout the year.
*Many birds fly to the tropics to escape cold
seasons in other parts of the world.*

tropopause *noun*
The tropopause is part of the Earth's
atmosphere. It marks the upper limit of
the **troposphere**. The tropopause lies about
18 kilometres above the **Equator**, but only
about 6 kilometres above the **poles**.
*The diagram of the sky marked the position of
the tropopause.*

troposphere *noun*
The troposphere is part of the Earth's
atmosphere. It can rise to about
18 kilometres above the Earth's surface.
The troposphere contains most of the
water **vapour** and **clouds** in the air.
Most weather occurs in the troposphere.

trough *noun*
A trough is a feature of **weather** systems.
It describes an area of low **atmospheric
pressure** which lies between two or more
areas of high pressure.
*The rain started to fall as the trough of low
pressure arrived.*

tsunami *noun*
A tsunami is a huge ocean **wave**. Tsunamis
are caused by movements of the sea floor
during **earthquakes** and volcanic **eruptions**.
They are particularly frequent around Japan
and the Philippines.
*Many people were drowned when the tsunami
struck the coast.*

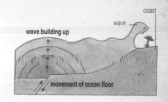

wave building up — coast — wave — *movement of ocean floor*

tundra *noun*
The tundra is a flat, northern **plain** where no
trees grow. The tundra is found between the
polar region and the **taiga** in Europe, North
America and Asia. The plants growing in the
tundra are mainly low shrubs, grasses,
mosses and lichens.
*When the weather became warm, the birds
flew north to breed on the tundra.*

tungsten *noun*
Tungsten is an **element**. It is a grey **metal**
which is found as a **compound** with **oxygen**.
Tungsten melts at higher **temperatures** than
any other metal. It is used to make **alloys** and
abrasives, and in some light bulbs. China is a
leading producer of tungsten.
*The steel was made harder after it was mixed
with a small amount of tungsten.*

turbulence *noun*
Turbulence is an uneven movement in water or air. It occurs when air or water flows rapidly past an object. The water in a **mountain stream** and the air in a **thunderstorm** are very turbulent.
The plane lurched suddenly in the air as it hit a pocket of turbulence.
turbulent *adjective*

turquoise *noun*
Turquoise is a **mineral**. It is light blue or blue-green in colour. Turquoise contains **copper**, **aluminium** and **phosphorus**. It is a semi-precious stone which can be used as a **gem**.
She wore a ring with a stone of blue turquoise at the centre.

twister ► **tornado**

typhoon ► **hurricane**

ultramarine *noun*
Ultramarine is a bright blue substance which is obtained from **lapis lazuli**. It is used as a blue colouring substance.
The artist chose ultramarine to give his painting a vivid blue sky.

undertow *noun*
Undertow is the backward movement of water below the surface of the **sea**. When a **wave** breaks on the **sea-shore**, the undertow drags backwards as the crest of the wave moves forwards.
The swimmers had to be very careful because of the dangerous undertow.

uranium *noun*
Uranium is an **element**. It is **radioactive** and is found in **pitchblende**. Uranium is the heaviest of all the elements found in nature. It is used for making nuclear energy.
The uranium was transported in sealed drums to the nuclear power station.

V

vacuum *noun*
A vacuum is a space which does not contain
matter. It is impossible to make a perfect
vacuum. However, **air** can be pumped out of
a container until it is nearly a vacuum. Outer
space is almost a vacuum.
*Heat cannot pass from one side of a vacuum
to another.*

valley *noun*
A valley is a trough-shaped dip in the
landscape. Most valleys contain a **river**.
A river creates its own valley as it slowly
erodes the rocks and soil beneath. Valleys
in high ground often have steep sides, but
lowland valleys are wide and gently curved.
The river lay at the bottom of a wide valley.

vapour *noun*
Vapour is the **gas** into which most liquids
change when they are heated. **Water** turns
into water vapour when it **evaporates** into
the **air**.
*After the storm, the air was full of water
vapour.*

varve *noun*
A varve is a banded layer of **silt** or **mud**.
It is deposited each year in **lakes**, especially
those near **ice-sheets**. Each varve has one
dark band and one light band. The dark band
is deposited in the **winter** and the lighter one
in the **summer**.
*The scientist counted the varves in the mud
to work out its age.*

vegetation *noun*
Vegetation is the total plant cover of an area
or region. It includes tiny mosses, grasses
and herbs, as well as the tallest trees.
As vegetation decomposes, it returns
minerals and other **chemicals** to the soil.
This forms **humus** and **peat**. **Tundra** and
tropical **rain forest** are two types of
vegetation.
*The fire destroyed all the vegetation in
its path.*

vein *noun*
A vein is a **seam** of **mineral** running through
a rock or stone. Veins are formed when liquids
rich in minerals flow through gaps in rocks
and become solid. The mineral in a vein often
contains useful **ores** which can be mined.
The vein contained iron ore.

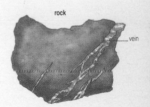

veld *noun*
Veld is a dry, open **grassland**. It is found on
the high **plateaux** of southern Africa. The veld
contains mainly grasses, with few trees.
*The farmer rode out across the veld to round
up his cattle.*

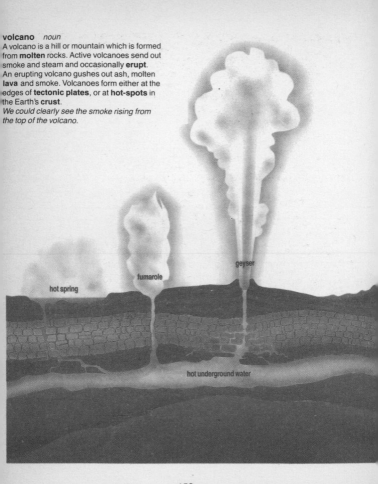

volcano *noun*
A volcano is a hill or mountain which is formed
from **molten** rocks. Active volcanoes send out
smoke and steam and occasionally **erupt**.
An erupting volcano gushes out ash, molten
lava and smoke. Volcanoes form either at the
edges of **tectonic plates**, or at **hot-spots** in
the Earth's **crust**.
*We could clearly see the smoke rising from
the top of the volcano.*

geyser

fumarole

hot spring

hot underground water

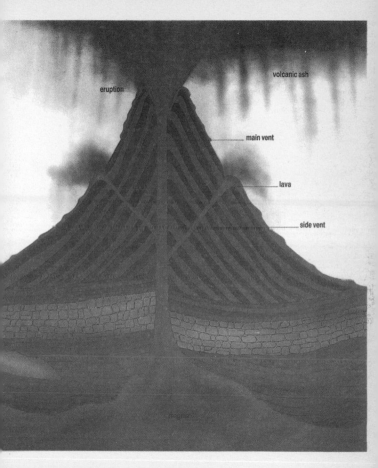

volcanic ash

eruption

main vent

lava

side vent

magma

vent *noun*
A vent is an air-hole or opening. Vents may be found in a **volcano**. When a volcano **erupts**, the **lava** comes out through a vent.
The lava gushed out of the vent and quickly covered the land nearby.

vermiculite *noun*
Vermiculite is a **mineral**. It contains **magnesium**, **aluminium** and **silicon**. When heated, vermiculite expands to become light and squashy. It is used for heat insulation and for packaging.
The precious vase was packed in vermiculite to stop it breaking during the journey.

volcanic *adjective*
Volcanic describes an area where the Earth's **crust** is active and where there are **volcanoes**. The crust is weak and there is molten rock, or **lava**, close to the surface. Volcanic areas may also have pools of boiling mud, or **geysers**, and hot water **springs**.
We visited Iceland and saw many areas of volcanic activity.

volcanic ash *noun*
Volcanic ash is the particles thrown into the air during the **eruption** of a **volcano**. Volcanic ash may rise to heights of about 20 or 30 kilometres in the **atmosphere**. The ash may travel a long distance in the air before it settles on the ground.
The people carried umbrellas to protect themselves from the volcanic ash.

volcano ▶ page 152

W

wadi *noun*
A wadi is a dried-up river bed in the **desert**. In a wadi, the water only flows occasionally, or not at all. Wadis usually fill with water only after heavy **rain** or flash floods.
The camels walked slowly along the wadi.

warm front *noun*
A warm front is the place where a mass of warm air moves over a mass of cold air. A warm front occurs when a **depression** arrives and brings warmer air and lower **atmospheric pressure**. As the warm air rises above the colder air, many **clouds** form and often produce rain.
The temperature rose as the warm front passed.

water *noun*
Water is a clear liquid with no smell or taste. It is made from **hydrogen** and **oxygen**. Water is mainly found in **seas**, **rivers**, **lakes**, and as **rain**. Many other **chemicals** dissolve in water. Solid water is called **ice**. When it is a **gas**, it is called water **vapour**. All life depends on water.
The trees could not grow without water.

water cycle *noun*
The water cycle is the process by which **water** leaves the **Earth's** surface and returns to it. Sunshine and wind cause water to **evaporate** from the surface of the sea and lakes as water **vapour**. This vapour forms **clouds** in the sky, which drop **rain** to the ground or sea. The water cycle is completed when the water flows through the ground in **streams** and **rivers** and back to the sea.
Without the water cycle, plants and animals could not live on dry land.

water level *noun*
Water level is the height of water in the **sea**, **rivers** or **lakes**. The water level in a lake or **reservoir** varies with the amount of **rainfall**.
The water level in the reservoir went down during the drought.

water table *noun*
The water table is the level to which **permeable** rocks are filled with **water** under the ground. **Wells** fill with water to the height of the water table. If the water table reaches the surface of the ground, water flows out of the ground as a **spring**.
Long periods of dry weather lowered the water table in the ground.

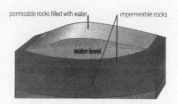

permeable rocks filled with water
impermeable rocks
water level

watercourse *noun*
A watercourse is a **channel** through which water flows, or has flowed in the past. Sometimes, an artificial watercourse is dug to change the direction of a **river**.
They built a new watercourse to divert the river around the town.

waterfall *noun*
A waterfall is a place in a **river** where the water drops steeply downwards. A waterfall often develops where the river flows over a band of hard rock. The river **erodes** the softer rock below and the waterfall slowly becomes bigger.
After the rains, the waterfall became much more powerful.

watershed *noun*
A watershed is the dividing line between two **drainage** systems. It occurs along the high ground between two **catchment areas**. The water on either side of the watershed flows into a different **river**.
From the ridge, we could see the rivers flowing from the watershed.

waterspout *noun*
A waterspout is a spinning column of **water** rising from the surface of the **sea** or a **lake**. A waterspout is a kind of **tornado**. When a tornado forms above water, or moves over water, it sucks water into the swirling air and makes a waterspout.
The waterspout sank the small boats as it passed across the lake.

wave *noun*
A wave describes the regular up-and-down movement of a substance. Waves are the ridges of water which move along on the surface of the **sea**. As a wave passes, the water rises and then falls again, until the next wave appears. Waves on the sea are caused by the wind and sometimes by the **tides**.
The high wind sent huge waves crashing against the coast.

wave breaking at coast
wave building up
land
sea

weather *noun*

Weather describes the condition of the
atmosphere in a particular place. The
weather can be cold, humid, wet, dry or
cloudy. Weather conditions such as these
are caused by **clouds**, **precipitation**,
temperature, **wind**, **humidity** and
atmospheric pressure.
The weather along the coast was very rainy.

temperature

air

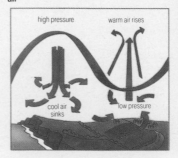

wind

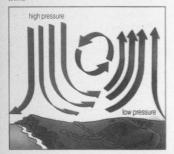

precipitation

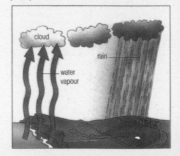

weather ▶ page 156

weather forecast *noun*
A weather forecast is a statement about what the **weather** is likely to be in the future. Weather forecasts usually predict the weather over the next few days. A weather forecast is based upon measurements of **atmospheric pressure**, **temperature** and **wind**. Satellites now measure changes in the weather from high above the Earth. These satellite measurements help to make weather forecasts more accurate over a longer period of time.
We went for a swim that day because the weather forecast was good.

weathering *noun*
Weathering is the gradual breaking down of **rocks** and **minerals** on the Earth's surface. Weathering turns rocks into **sand** and **soil**. The action of wind, water, ice or **chemical** reactions can cause weathering.
The cliff had been shaped by many thousands of years of weathering.

well *noun*
A well is a deep hole dug in the ground. Wells are dug to reach a liquid or gas lying below the surface. Some wells provide water, others are made to reach **deposits**, such as **crude oil** and **natural gas**.
They drilled a deep well through the Earth's crust in order to reach the oil.

westerlies *noun*
The westerlies are kinds of **wind**. The westerlies are winds that blow from a westerly direction. They are found between **latitudes** of about 40 and 70 degrees north and south of the **Equator**. In the **northern hemisphere**, they blow mostly from the south-west. In the **southern hemisphere**, they blow from the north-west. Winds called the Roaring Forties are examples of westerlies in the southern hemisphere.
The westerlies brought a series of depressions towards the continent.

wetland *noun*
A wetland is any area of **land** in which the surface is normally filled with **water**. Wetlands include **bogs**, **marshes** and **swamps**. A wetland may contain fresh water or salt water, depending upon where it is.
The wetland covered the floor of the valley.

whirlpool *noun*
A whirlpool is a circular **current** in a river or sea. It is caused by currents, **tides** or **winds** moving in opposite directions. A whirlpool will drag floating objects down into its centre.
We could not swim because of the whirlpool.

movement of current

whirlwind ▶ tornado

wilderness *noun*
A wilderness is a **region** which is uninhabited and uncultivated. A wilderness may be a dry, sandy **desert** or an area of **snow** and **ice**, such as **Antarctica**. A **rain forest** may be called a wilderness if it is unaltered by people.
Antarctica is one of the last areas of wilderness left on the Earth.

wind ▶ page 158

winter *noun*
Winter is the coldest **season** of the year in a **temperate** climate. Winter is also the time when the days are shortest. In the **northern hemisphere**, winter lasts from about November to February. In the **southern hemisphere**, winter lasts from about May to August.
In winter, the snow covered the land and the rivers turned to ice.

wind *noun*

Wind is movement of the **air**. Wind moves air from an area of **high pressure** to one of **low pressure**. **Polar** winds are cold winds which blow down from the **Arctic** and **Antarctica**. **Trade winds** are **tropical** and blow towards the Equator. Many winds are regular and have local names, like the **mistral** and the **sirocco** in the Mediterranean regions. Wind force is measured on the **Beaufort Scale**.
The hot air balloon began to pick up speed as the wind increased.

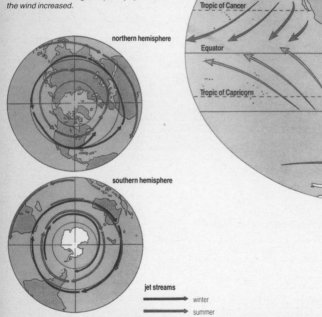

northern hemisphere

Tropic of Cancer

Equator

Tropic of Capricorn

southern hemisphere

jet streams

→ winter

→ summer

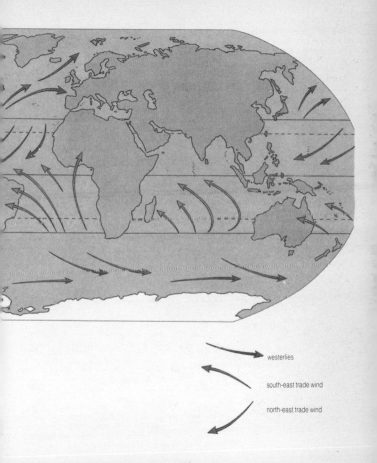

westerlies

south-east trade wind

north-east trade wind

wood *noun*

Wood is the substance from which **tree** trunks are made. Wood contains a **chemical** called cellulose which gives it strength. Wood is a valuable **natural resource** which is used for building and as a **fuel**. Wood is also used to make paper.

They planted pines in a large plantation to provide them with a supply of wood.

pine

sycamore

trunk

Z

zenith *noun*

The zenith is an imaginary point in the sky. The zenith lies vertically overhead. It is also the highest point reached by a planet or the Sun above a point on the Earth's surface.

At midday, the Sun reached its zenith.

Sun's zenith

zinc *noun*

Zinc is an **element**. It is a bluish-white **metal** and is poisonous. Zinc is used to coat **iron** and steel. It is also used in medicines.

The metal coin contained zinc combined with copper.

zircon *noun*

Zircon is a **mineral**. It contains the **element** zirconium. Zircon is hard and heavy, and normally has a brown colour. It is found as **crystals** in **igneous** and **metamorphic** rocks. Some forms of zircon are colourless and are used as semi-precious stones.

The children collected a few grains of zircon from the sandy beach.

zone *noun*

A zone is a series of **layers** in **rocks**. Each zone may be distinguished by a particular collection of **fossils**.

As we moved along the cliff into a new zone, we found several new fossils.